TURKEYS AT

by

Michael and Victoria Roberts

Illustrated by:
Sara Roadnight

Photographs by:
Michael Roberts

Cover Photograph:
A bronze turkey stag and a white turkey stag
at the Domestic Fowl Trust.
(Michael Roberts)

Published by The Domestic Fowl Trust

Printed by Philip Bennett Lithographic Printers Ltd.
Stratford-upon-Avon.

ISBN 0 947870 06 7

Contents

INTRODUCTION

Not only small farmers are considering rearing a few turkeys for Christmas with the current trend for alternative farming enterprises. The market for the small producer has increased with the desire and awareness of the consumer to eat naturally reared turkeys fed on natural feed. It is always easier to come to terms with rearing birds for food if it is borne in mind from the outset that a particular group is destined for the table: you know they have had a good life, you know what they have been fed on and you know they will not be stressed before killing.

As individuals, we have found turkeys are highly intelligent and great companions. They have a strong mischievous streak which can be both destructive and infuriating, but their flock instinct is powerful which makes them good guards. Altogether a fascinating bird.

Michael and Victoria Roberts
The Domestic Fowl Trust
Honeybourne, 1989

The origin of the name: **TURKEY**

While the correct origin of the word has not been irrefutably established, here are several interesting theories of possible derivations:

1. the mis-pronunciation of the Red Indian word for turkey - "firkee".
2. because the bird was new (in Europe) and looked, perhaps, something akin to a turkish soldier, a "turkoman" (Victorian legend).
3. the call the bird makes. (Anyone who has kept turkeys knows they don't go "turk, turk", but "keow, keow").
4. "Turkish" being slang for something foreign.
5. a mix-up in the Latin names of turkeys and guinea fowl, both thought to come originally from Turkey.
6. the Tamil word in India for peacock being "Tali".
7. the Aramaic-Jewish word for bustard (*Otis tarda*) "Tahki". This last one rather appeals as the nearest to the truth as the bulk of domestic turkeys arrived in Spain (in approx. 1511) and people have a habit of calling something new after something they know.

HISTORY OF TURKEYS

Origin: Northern and Central America

The Aztec Indians of Mexico who lived in cities first domesticated the turkey and kept them in huge flocks. The birds were not only kept for their flesh but also for their feathers, an important part of Aztec culture. Being one of the few domesticated creatures at that time, they were revered by the Aztecs and used as subjects for paintings; place names containing the Aztec word for turkey - Toto - can still be found in that area.

There are six subspecies of turkey, only two varieties playing a part in the make-up of the domestic bird. *Meleagris gallopavo gallopavo* is the nominate race and found in Mexico and was the basis of the domestic turkey. The other subspecies was *Meleagris gallopavo silvestris* which had a huge range on the wooded eastern seaboard stretching from the southern states bordering the Gulf of Mexico up to Canada. *Silvestris* has brown instead of white in the tail feathers. The Latin name is shared with guinea fowl (*Numidia meleagris*) presumably because both guineas and turkeys have the same naked head and neck. Then *gallo* from *gallus*, a cock, and *pavo*, a peafowl -rather more fanciful, but probably mimicking the raising of the tail feathers in display.

The eastern wild turkey was never domesticated to the same extent by the north American Indians as they were mainly nomadic. The turkeys were very plentiful and it was not until the advent of the gun that they became shy. Among the Cherokee Indians, turkey was the prey of children, adults having more difficult prey to cope with. The birds were "called up" by imitating their calls, and then grabbed by the legs by a child hiding behind some logs or in a pit, or shot with bow and arrow. The wild turkey is still hunted today by the method of calling up which is more difficult than it sounds and in some States there are turkey calling competitions, not as you may think judged by turkeys but by people who know the birds and their habits best, the hunters.

The abundance of turkey played a part in the diet of the first arrivals from Europe and has since always been associated with Thanksgiving Day.

The arrival of the first turkeys into England is attributed to William Strickland of Yorkshire. Son of Roger Strickland of Marsk, William was inspired by the Cabot's voyages, *circa* 1497, to the New World and sailed later, about 1520, bringing some turkeys back home with him. The first known date of turkeys in England is about 1524 when "it happened that diverse things were newly brought to England, whereupon this rhyme was made: Turkeys, Carps, Hoppes, Piccarell and Beer, came in England all in one year." William Strickland made a fortune from his voyages, buying land extensively near to Bridlington and Boynton Hall in 1549. Durings the Herald's visit to Yorkshire in 1550 William Strickland was granted a coat of arms which includes a 'Turkey cock in its pride'. He became MP for Scarborough in 1558 and died and was buried, together with his wife Elizabeth, at Wintringham, near Malton in 1598. The church of Boynton contains a stained glass window of a turkey, together with a wooden lectern with a carved turkey instead of the normal eagle, but this is a memorial to Frederick Strickland who died in the 1930s. A branch of the Strickland family headed south to Deerhurst, near Tewkesbury, in the 1750s and a small stone carved turkey can be found in the church there. (See inside back cover).

Adult female Buff Turkeys

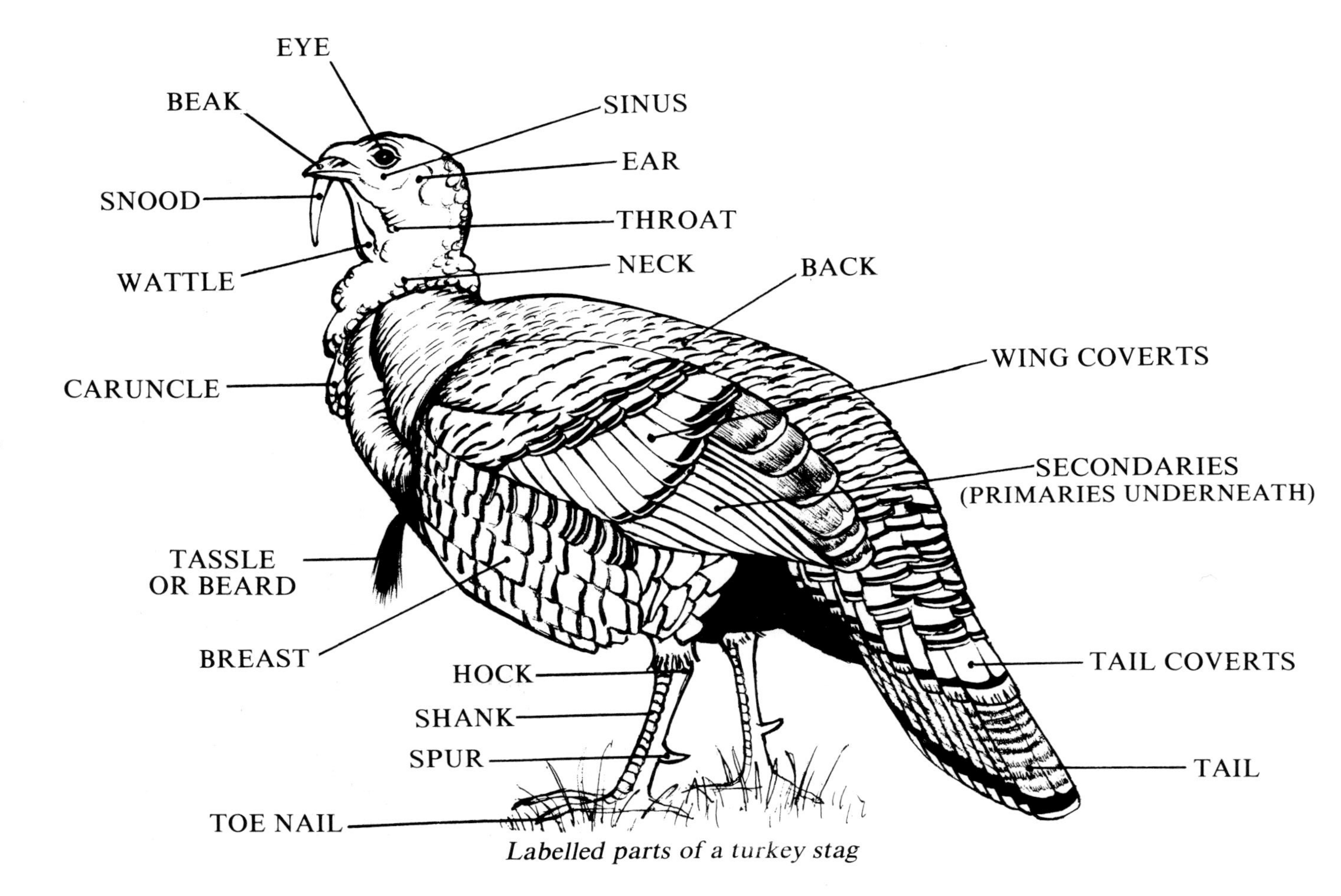

Labelled parts of a turkey stag

CHARACTERISTICS AND BEHAVIOUR PATTERNS

Of all the domestic fowl, turkeys are probably the most vocal and have some unusual characteristics. They have higher blood pressure than other fowl, so care must be taken that they are not chased as they can suffer a heart attack, particularly the heavier stags, quite easily. They are slowly drivable as their flock instinct is strong.

The best known call of the turkey is the "gobble" made by the stags. From an early age there is the pitiful "weepe, weepe" call when a chick or poult has got out or left behind, which develops into "keow, keow" as an adult. The alarm call is a "putt, putt" in both sexes. When fighting, the stags are very vocal, starting with a light cooing noise through to various yelps. The hen which is being mated will squeal "yee, yee". There is another call by the stags of "crok, crok" which is a warning call, tinged with curiosity.

From very young, turkeys will display and play. They tame very easily and are gentle when eating out of your hand. It is funny to see three week old chicks fanning their tails and dropping their wings. It is no indicator of sex at this age as aggressive hens will also display. The young stags usually display more often. As the wings develop there are all sorts of games including King of the Castle, dancing, mock fighting, bullying and even killing other birds. They are insatiably curious and will often get themselves into mischief with this inquisitive streak.

Young stags will spend much time sparring unless an older bird is put with them to keep the peace. When they fight they lock their beaks or lock onto the other's snood or neck and hang on and pull unmercifully. Care should be taken that there is enough food and feeding space when they are adolescent for this reason. Young hens are more vocal than stags and then become less vocal as they mature. "Gobbling" in stags starts from 10-16 weeks. The familiar display of the stags - fanned tail, dropped wings, snood down - is not aggressive but a way to attract the females and appear more majestic than the others. The "poomf" noise thay make when displaying is a displacement of air in the region of the crop. When the hen is ready to be mated, she quickly crouches on the floor. Some hens are more willing than others which can lead to torn backs if saddles are not fitted. The colouring on the stag's head can change colour according to mood from bright scarlet to white to blue to pink.

Sexing: when hatching your own birds or buying in as hatched you will have to wait until 10-12 weeks to be certain of sexing turkeys correctly. Although the stags redden up faster than the hens it is still possible to make mistakes at this age. The heads of the hens are smaller and finer than the stags and there are more feathers on the heads of the hens. On being picked up the hens are more vocal. Bronze poults have white barring on the breast feathers (both sexes) until the stags moult into a dark breast. The hens retain the barring. The longer length of the shank can indicate males at a young age. It is possible to obtain professionally sexed day olds, but not essential from a marketing point of view as differing weights will be wanted by the customer.

Catching: The least stressful way of catching a turkey both for you and the bird is to use a fishing landing net. They never realise how long your arm is. With the older and heavier birds it is best quietly and slowly to corner them and grab the legs. Let the bird rest on its breast while you get a good grip on its legs and then gently swing the bird up and under your arm, holding the wings firmly between your upper arm and body as they can give you an awful clout. It is advisable to plan the distance of carrying turkeys carefully as they are extremely heavy. Turkey muck is particularly pungent, probably due to the high grass content in their diet, so keep the tail pointing away from you.

Always remember that turkeys are very strong with sharp claws and need to be handled firmly but gently.

Young stags and hens

BREEDS AND VARIETIES

All of the varieties of domestic turkey owe their origin to the wild turkey *Meleagris gallopavo gallopavo* found in Mexico. There are five subspecies which vary slightly in colour and are distributed through central and north America.

Domestic turkeys can be divided into two distinct types: coloured and commercial white. There are many varieties of coloured turkeys all of which breed true including black, bronze, white, blue, blue laced, slate, black and white, buff, buff laced, copper, red, red and black, spotted. The names given to these colours vary from country to country and what we call Pied (black and white) in England is known as Crollwitzer in Germany and Royal Palm in America. Growth rate of the coloured varieties is slower than the commercial white but they do seem to be hardier and do better on free range.

Commercial White

The name of the strain differs depending on which company you go to. There are three types of commercial turkey: small, medium and heavy, suitable for intensive conditions, all white feathered so they pluck cleanly. These attain various weights in set times and this is important when marketing. The small strains reach 9lbs for stags and 7lbs for hens in 12 weeks, the medium strains reach 16lbs for stags and 11lbs for hens in 16 weeks and the heavies weigh in at 30lbs or more at 24 weeks. (Record heaviest in 1988 was 84¼lb!). In direct contrast to the reason white feathered birds were developed (the dark pin feathers of the bronze, the common meat producing turkey of the time, were considered unattractive to the housewife) some commercial hatcheries are marketing a few bronze poults as these with their dark pin feathers are instantly recognisable and put forward as being more likely to have been range reared.

Bronze

The colour nearest to its ancester, the wild turkey, and various strains of bronze were developed in the 1930's with various growth rates such as Cambridge, Mammoth, Broadbreasted, before the advent of the commercial white. It is considered to be the most spectacularly coloured of all the turkeys with irridescent green, brown, red, black and white.

Norfolk Black

This is the traditional East Anglian meat type and has been bred there for centuries. The chicks and poults are the most attractive of the young coloured turkeys having white faces and primaries and black bodies. The white gradually moults out until the birds are a dense black all over.

Lavender: even light blue all over.

Slate: even grey blue all over, may be dotted with black.

Black and White (Pied, Royal Palm or Crollwitzer): white with black bars.

Buff: cinnamon colour with white wings and a white tail bar.

Red (Bourbon Red, Ronquières): rich mahogany red with black bars, white wings and tail, brown bar on tail.

Spotted (Nebraskan): white with black and red flecks.

Black wing (Crimson Dawn): bronze in colour with black wings and a pink/crimson tinge.

Narragansett: similar to Bronze but the bronze colour is replaced with steel grey.

The genetics of colour production is fascinating and "sports" (odd colours) can be thrown by any of these colours even if they have been bred pure for generations.

Advantages and disadvantages of coloured and commercial white turkeys.

Coloured

Pro	Con
hardy	higher bone to meat ratio
eat more grass, better flavour	limited quantities only available April-June
attractive	dark colours leave dark stubs (more of an advantage as it is more likely to be free range)
breed your own	have to pay for their winter keep
easier to manage for novice	stock might be inbred
premium if organic	

Commercial white

Pro	Con
available all year round	extra management, novices beware
different sizes	not too good on outdoor systems
high meat to bone ratio	not easy to find small quantities of stock
pluck clean	have to buy in
on the farm a limited time	eat more when confined
	flavour not as good

NUTRITION

Requirements of turkeys for differing amounts of the main feed components varies with age and stage of production but the basic principles are the same.

There are five requirements:

1. Energy
2. Amino acids ('building units' of body proteins)
3. Minerals
4. Vitamins
5. Water

Both energy and protein are needed for *maintenance* i.e. muscular movement, heart beat, nervous system, maintenance of body temperature, and for *production* which may be in the form of weight gain or egg production.

1. **Energy** is measured in terms of Digestible Energy and the units are megajoules (MJ) (one joule is like a calorie so think of it as mega calories). Digestible Energy is that which is digested e.g. 1Kg of food containing 18MJ is eaten. 6MJ of energy is found to be in the droppings. Therefore the Digestible Energy of this food is 12MJ per Kg (18 minus 6). Feed for turkeys must be balanced to produce the number of MJ of Digestible Energy (DE) supplied with the energy requirement at a particular stage of growth or production.

2. **Protein** is built up of amino acids. There are about 20 types. Each body protein is composed of a very specific sequence of amino acids. About 10 can be manufactured in the liver i.e. it is not essential they are absorbed from the gut. About 10 *cannot* be manufactured within the tissues of the bird, these are termed ESSENTIAL amino acids i.e. it is essential that they are absorbed from the gut. During digestion enzymes in the gut break the proteins down to amino acids. A shortage of one of the essential amino acids will adversely affect the rate at which body protein is produced and therefore of production. The diet must supply all the essential amino acids. This is expressed as % crude protein which is a statutory measurement but is of limited value as it indicates nothing of the *quality* of the dietary protein. You can see from Table 1 that the fish-meal has the highest values, but it is expensive, so other items are used instead or as well as to keep the price down which in theory should not affect the quality of the feed but in practice can do sometimes. The energy to protein ratio must also be balanced. Fortunately, the birds have the ability to decide how much energy they need, providing they are fed to appetite, so in cold weather they will eat more.

Table 1 Nutrient levels of ingredients commonly found in turkey rations

Items	Digestible energy (MJ/kg)	Crude protein (%)	Essential Amino Acids: Lysine (%)	Methionine (%)	Tryptophan (%)	Calcium (%)	Available phosphorus (%)
Wheat	12.5	11.0	0.35	0.15	0.12	0.07	0.13
Barley	11.5	9.9	0.38	0.15	0.13	0.07	0.13
Maize	12.9	8.5	0.24	0.19	0.05	0.02	0.08
Oats	10.5	9.4	0.42	0.18	0.13	0.08	0.14
Fish 66	12.5	63.0	4.40	1.70	0.60	5.00	3.00
Meat & Bone	9.3	50.0	2.00	0.70	0.26	8.00	4.00
Full Fat Soya	14.1	40.1	2.30	0.52	0.52	0.24	0.31
Extracted Soya	10.0	44.6	3.04	0.61	0.58	0.27	0.62
Dehulled Soya	10.5	48.6	3.16	0.66	0.63	0.27	0.40

Feed formulation is a highly specialised job involving many more details than are in Table 1, but it probably helps if you understand the basic requirements and can 'translate' the label on the bag. See page 13.

3. **Minerals:** most important are calcium and phosphorus and these should be correctly provided in commercial feed and will vary with the age of the turkey.

4. **Vitamins:** adequate amounts will be mixed into commercial feed which will be alright for the turkeys kept indoors, but you will always find range turkeys supplementing with different types of plants and insects.

5. **Water:** vital to all processes and should be provided clean and fresh.

The digestive system of turkeys contains a limited system for digesting grass and plants. There are bacteria in the blind gut or caeca (there are two of these) which help to break down the fibre in the plants. Turkeys graze much more than chickens and search out clover, plantain and even thistles and consume them with relish. As this digestive system is limited the bulk of the diets are cereal based with added protein.

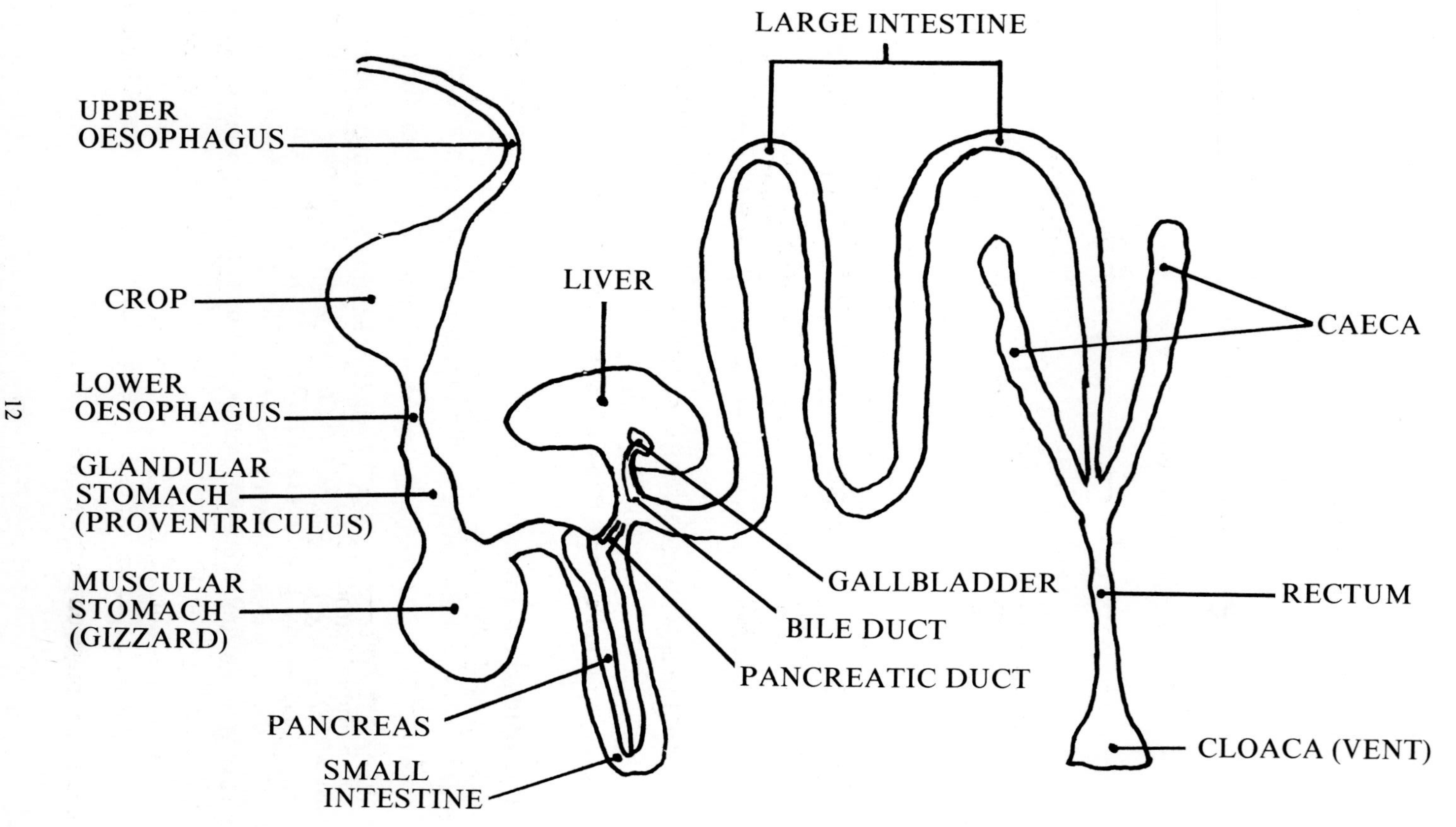

Digestive system of the turkey

Feed bag label example

A1437637

25 kg net **BOCM SILCOCK**
BASINGSTOKE HAMPSHIRE

613 Turkey Starter Crumbs ACS ABS

% OIL	% PROTEIN	% FIBRE	% ASH
6	26	3	7

The following Vitamin levels are guaranteed until the end of **JULY 85**
Vitamin A 10,000 iu/kg Vitamin D3 5,000 iu/kg Vitamin E 33 iu/kg.
This compound feedingstuff contains 1.0mg/kg molybdenum, 0.35mg/kg selenium and a permitted antioxidant.
FOR FEEDING TO GROWING TURKEYS.

DO NOT FEED TO TURKEYS OVER 16 WEEKS OF AGE OR WITHIN 6 DAYS OF SLAUGHTER BUT REPLACE WITH A BOCM SILOCK WITHDRAWAL BRAND. DO NOT FEED TO GUINEA FOWL OR OTHER AVIAN SPECIES, OR TO CHICKENS OR TURKEYS PRODUCING EGGS, OR TO HORSES OR OTHER EQUINES-INGESTION OF MONENSIN BY HORSES HAS BEEN FATAL, DO NOT TREAT BIRDS BEING FED THIS FEEDINGSTUFF WITH PRODUCTS CONTAINING TIAMULIN, OR FEED THIS FEEDINGSTUFF WITHIN 7 DAYS OF TREATMENT WITH TIAMULIN-MAY BE FATAL.
20mg/kg avoparcin (Avotan 50(R) PL0095/4026) was added as a growth promoter and 125mg/kg dimetridazole (Emtryl Pure PL0012/4174) as an aid in the prevention of blackhead and 90mg/kg monensin (Elancoban Premix PL0006/4047) as an aid in the prevention of coccidiosis.

Store in a cool dry place. In case of complaint, please return this label. 613ap/04

Food components in relation to requirements

Diet Analysis → **Requirement**

1. Water → Water
2. Dry Matter

* (a) Oils & Fats → Energy
(b) 'Soluble' Carbohydrates (starch & sugars) → Energy
* (c) Crude Fibre (fibrous carbohydrates) - - → Energy
* (d) Crude Protein → Amino Acids
* (e) Ash → Minerals
(does not burn, therefore not energy)
(f) Vitamins → Vitamins

* is the percentage on the bag label

BREEDING

It is important to select good birds for the breeding pen. Aim for uniformity in size, shape and colour. All birds should be handled individually checking head, eyes, beak, down the neck, breast bone, back, flanks, thighs, wings, tail and vent (fleas?). In all try to ensure that the bird feels fit and well fleshed with no old wounds on the flanks from a previous year's over enthusiastic stag. Be careful not to inbreed, ensuring that birds are unrelated by changing stags regularly, say every two years.

Turkeys will lay between 50 and 100 eggs a year. In theory, three good laying hens will produce 250 poults. In practice, it doesn't work quite like that, certainly not all in a uniform batch. This may or may not be an advantage depending on your market e.g. if you are supplying a hotel with a few birds each week, disparate ages will help to keep the continuity of supply. When you are planning your meat-producing birds it is important to hatch in batches which are compatible with your sales requirements and working this in with existing incubator space. This could mean a lot of eggs being used in a short period, large batches of equal weight birds, or small batches of eggs over a long period. Do not forget that if batches are of mixed sexes they will be of mixed weights.

Say that you have found a market for 200 Norfolk Black birds, mixed weights for the Christmas market and you want to breed your own, it would be useful to ensure that the breeding programme including the cost of keeping the breeding stock throughout the year, is profitable. The way to do this is to hatch double or treble your own requirements and sell the surplus either at day old or as off heat poults, preferably a good distance from where your market is. If you have a stag and eight hens the egg output from those birds should be enough to hatch 500-600 chicks. The weekly egg production should be 30-45 eggs, depending on diet and length of daylight. Turkeys naturally lay from April to June or July, but a few March eggs will produce some heavier birds by Christmas.

Young birds are better to breed from as they are normally more fertile and produce more eggs. (The youngest a hen turkey can lay an egg is 30 weeks old). The ratio of stags to hens can range from 1:2 up to 1:18 in the lighter breeds. In the case of heavier breeds like the heavy whites or bronze, a "saddle" may have to be fitted to the hens. This protects them from the claws of the stag which can rip the back and sides of hens leaving gaping 2″ - 6″ holes with torn skin and rendering further mating impossible. We have not found saddles necessary in the lighter, coloured breeds, except where there were too few hens or too many stags. The saddle is made of canvas fitted around and under the wings with two canvas loops. There is no cruelty here, but protection, and the birds just wear them during the breeding season. Saddles can be marked with large lettering for easy individual identification. If a stag or stags are kept away from the breeding pen without hens they are sometimes to be seen imitating the act of treading. This includes stamping on the ground, wings down, back arched, with a mewing call and is quite normal. An older stag kept with younger ones will act as a "policeman" and keep the peace.

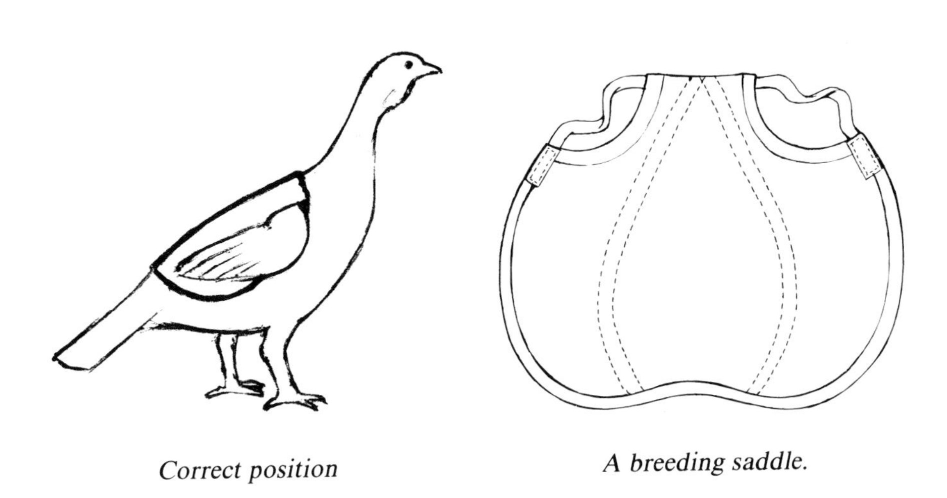

Correct position *A breeding saddle.*

Suitable nestboxes must be provided, a bank of four or more on the floor and the size being 18″ x 18″ x 24″ high. The litter inside can be straw or shavings. Lighting is important in the early part of the year to ensure good egg production. The sperm production of the males is also affected by lighting, so don't forget to include them. Lighting should start on 1st February, a month before the time required for the first eggs, increasing the existing day length by one hour per week to a maximum of 14 hours. A 40 watt bulb being enough for an area 10′ x 10′. Care should be taken to collect the eggs twice a day so that thay are clean and damage is kept to a minimum. Also to discourage broodiness. Hen turkeys will go broody readily and any broody birds should be removed from the breeding pen to the "sin-bin" which is a coop 2′ x 3′ x 2′ high with a slatted floor. Water and food must be available all the time through the bars of the coop, and after a week the turkey should be ready to return to the breeding pen.

It is well worth recording the number of eggs laid on a daily basis which can then be added to your records of eggs set and hatched. It is easier to spot any problems if proper records are kept and used.

If you have the time and the interest, further recording can be made by trap-nesting individual hens as they lay. There are several different designs but basically the idea is to hold the bird after it has laid its egg so that the egg can be marked, recorded and identified with the hen, leading to detailed production, fertility or pedigree records. Numbered wing tags are useful for individual recording.

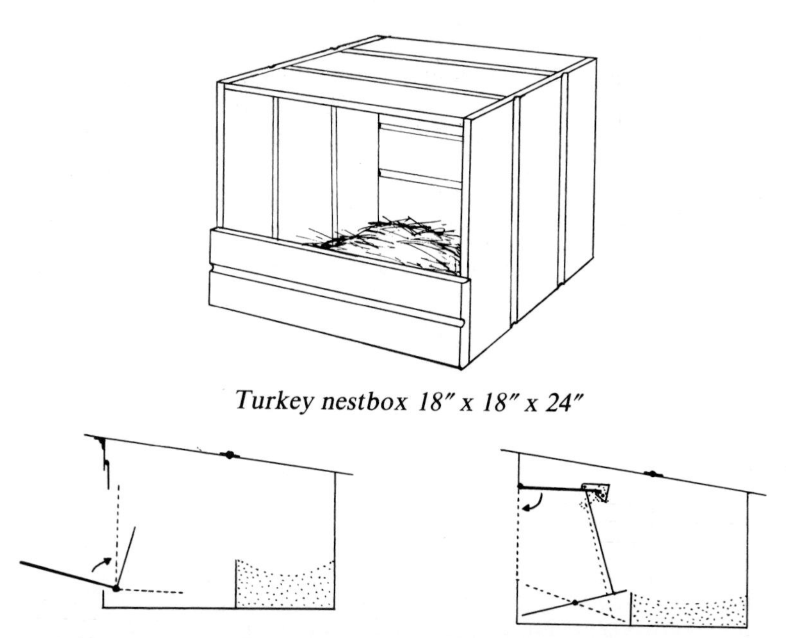

Turkey nestbox 18″ x 18″ x 24″

Two types of trapnest. Make them long enough so the hen bird does not stand on the eggs while trying to get out, and take the egg out before you remove the bird.

It must be understood that trap-nesting is very time consuming as the nest boxes must be checked every two hours and the birds released.

Feeding of breeding birds needs to be carefully monitored with a breeders pellet added to the ration at least six weeks before the first egg is expected. This will ensure strong embryos and chicks. Do not forget to keep mixed grit, soluble and insoluble, in front of the birds at all times.

Artificial Insemination is used in large breeding establishments due to the size of the stags, but it is not necessary with the smaller coloured turkeys.

HOUSING

Water: One hundred turkeys will drink upwards of 18 gallons of water a day, so automatic drinkers are useful, bearing in mind an alternative system must be at hand when all the pipes freeze.
Security: Unfortunately this is an important aspect not only against the four-legged fox but the two-legged as well. Simple alarm systems are available. Turkeys caught at night are uncharacteristically quiet, so try adding a few guinea fowl as watchdogs.

Housing for breeding

1. **Shed or barn** divided into breeding pens with access to pasture if possible. Allow 12 sq ft per bird, straw or shavings as litter, with 3′ high solid divisions between pens with wire netting above for best ventilation. The solid part prevents the stags fighting through the wire. Their strong legs and feet will break chicken wire very quickly. Perches should be 2′ high and made of 2″ x 2″ or 2″ x 3″ timber, allowing 18″ per bird. Nest boxes should be provided one for every four hens, 18″ x 18″ x 24″ high.

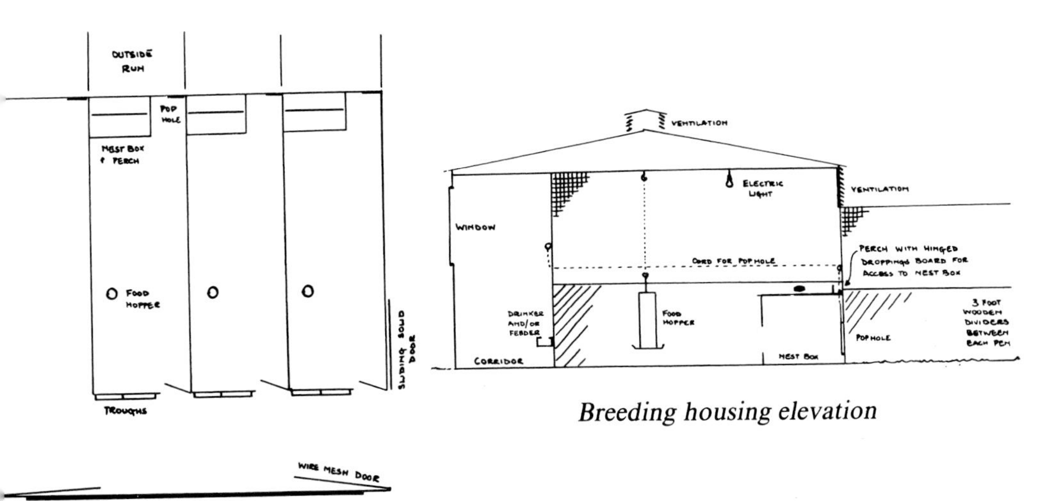

Breeding housing elevation

Breeding housing plan.

2. **Verandah** - a useful system where space is limited as the birds are separated from their droppings and from the soil. The birds can be caught using a leg crook.

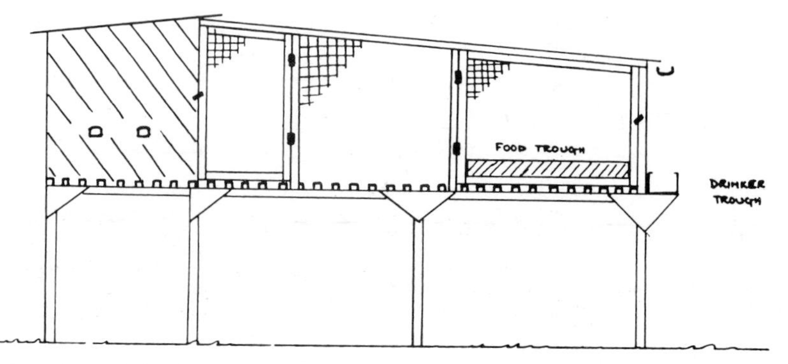

Rearing Verandah 12′ x 6′ x 3′6″ rising to 4′, 3′ off the ground.
Must be sited in a sheltered area with plenty of sunlight. The roof of the run can be covered with corrugated perspex. Suitable for 12-16 birds depending on final weight.

Housing for rearing

1. **Shed** - 25 dayolds will need 3′ x 3′ which must be increased to 12′ x 10′ for 25 mature birds, i.e. 5 sq ft per bird. A stable door is useful as an entrance/exit, allowing them access to pasture, and the top can be closed at night or left open with a wire screen for security. Draught free ventilation is vital, best situated above the heads of the birds. Perches should be made of 2″ x 2″ or 2″ x 3″ timber and put 2′ high. Turkeys like to perch at night but not necessarily indoors, unlike chickens, so they need to be trained from an early age.

Young turkeys and hens in a stable

2. **Free range behind fox-proof perimeter fence** - a simple field shelter is all that is needed with wind protection and some rain protection. Turkeys will tolerate showers with equanimity but dislike prolonged rain. 10′ x 10′ will accommodate 50 mature birds. They will attempt to roost in trees if these are within reach. One clipped wing will keep their roosting activities within bounds. The shelter is designed to be movable and should be sited with its back to the prevailling wind. You may have to turn the shelter in the winter to the SW if a strong and persistent northerly gets up, for instance.

Range shelter for a fox proof area

Wing Clipping

Kitchen scissors are the easiest to use, clip one wing only, and just the primary feathers. There is a convenient line of small feathers which if you use them as a guide you will clip in the correct place.

Wing clipping

Three styles of fox-proof fencing.

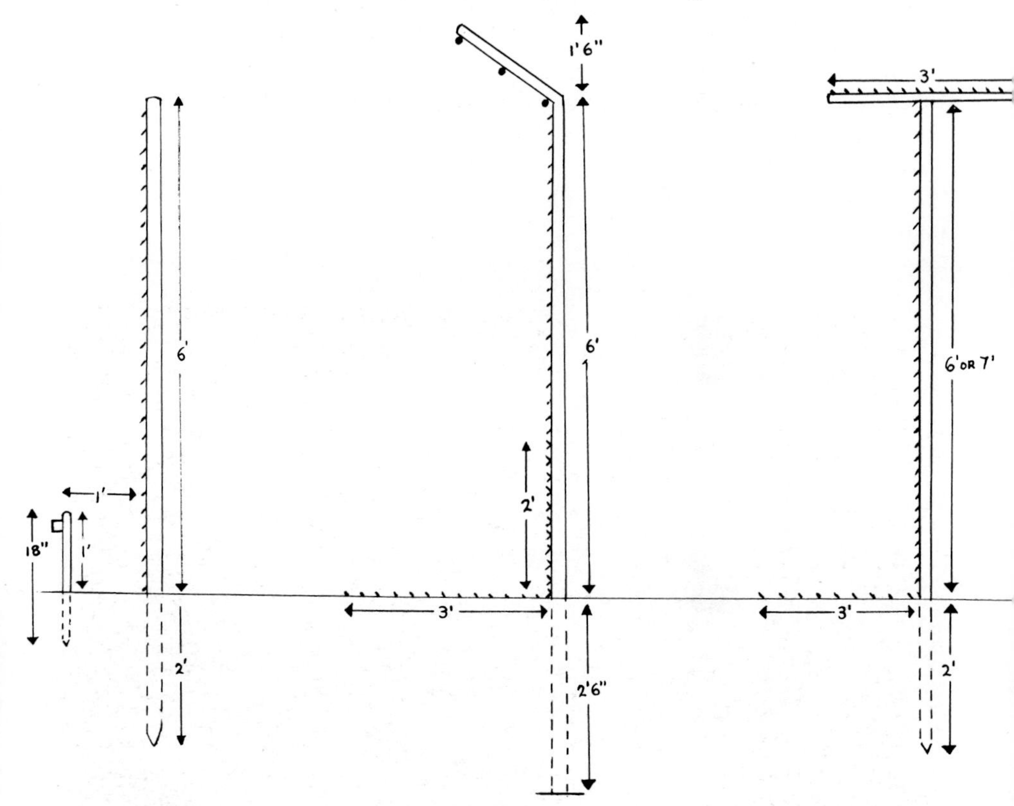

1. 8′ wooden posts with 6′2″ mesh wire netting and electric fence.

2. 2″ x 2″ angle iron with three strands of barbed wire at the top, then chain lnk or 2″ wire mesh with 5′ x 1″ wire mesh on ground and up the side.

3. 8′ or 9′ wooden posts with 3′ x 1″ mesh wire on top, then pig or sheep wire then 5′ or 6′ x 1″ mesh on ground and up the side.

Plastic electrified netting 4′ high such as Flexinet is quite useful for keeping the turkeys to a designated area as long as the pulse unit is powerful. It is not 100% fox proof.

3. **Pole barn** - the most popular way of housing fattening turkeys. The construction is simple cheap and quick. Allow 5 sq ft per bird and no more than 200 birds in a section. This helps when catching them as in a large bunch they will suffocate each other in their attempt to get away from the catcher. The smaller units are useful in phasing the production of the birds.

12 week old fattening turkeys in a pole barn

The same barn from the outside

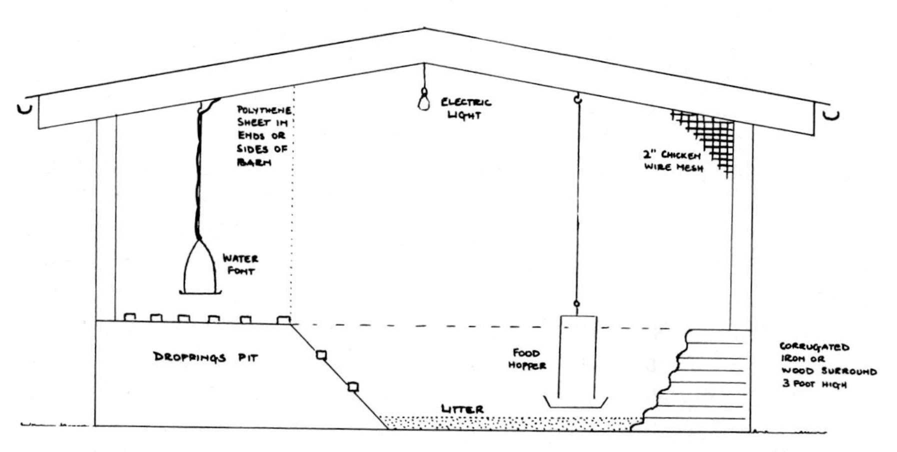

Diagram of a pole barn. Note the water font is over the droppings pit in case of spillage.

4. **Fold Units:** likely to be unwieldy due to the size needed and not economic for a few birds.

HATCHING

There are three methods of hatching turkey eggs:

1. under a broody chicken
2. under a broody turkey
3. in an incubator

The eggs of a turkey are large (average 88g or 3-3½oz) with defined blunt and pointed ends and brown freckles on a cream background. The incubation period is 28 days. Storage should be blunt end up in a temperature of 50 degrees F (10 degrees C) for up to 7 days, or turned end over end if stored longer. Or prop up first one side then the other of egg trays at about 30 degrees. Storage after 14 days reduces hatchability. If the eggs are very dirty do not set them. Small amounts of dirt can be removed by sandpaper. Washing is not recommended, but if considered necessary use water warmer than the eggs: this is to ensure that the membrane inside the shell expands on contact with the warmer water, helping to exclude bacteria. If you use colder water than the egg the membrane shrinks and draws any bacteria in through the shell which of course is porous. Set only good sized, normal shaped eggs.

1. **Under a broody chicken**

This is the traditional way and often gives the best results, as long as you have enough hens broody at the right time.

Broody boxes are best constructed as per the diagram and with wire netting on the base to prevent rats from burrowing into the nest. They are best set directly onto the earth which allows beneficial natural moisture to come up through the nest. The boxes can be made in banks of any number, but four or five makes for easy handling before and after the hatching season. The boxes should be set on a small mound, about two turves high, in case there is a lot of rain, and in the shade. They must not get too hot as this is likely to put the broody off. Punch a shallow dip like a saucer in a turf and lay this, grass side down, in the box. Line the depression thinly with sweet hay or straw. Make sure the turf fits well so that no eggs can get rolled out into the cold. Put crock eggs or marked fresh eggs into the nest ready for the broody; she needs to sit steady on these for a few days before you put in the eggs you want her to hatch.

A bank of broody boxes

Select your broody from as large a breed as possible such as Sussex, Cochin, Orpington, Rhode Island Red, as using Silkies or Silkie crosses will limit the number of eggs you can set due to their small size. Although some Hybrid hens have been known to sit well they are on the whole totally unreliable. Broodies will not want to leave their nest if they are serious and will guard any eggs jealously fluffing up their feathers and grumbling at you, even pecking at intruding hands. In order to check that your selected broody is serious, take any eggs out and slide your hand under her, palm up. She should "cuddle" your hand with her wings. You must delouse with Cooper's louse powder any broody before getting her to sit for you as she will otherwise be irritated and disturbed by fleas. If your broodies are not used to being handled it is best to put them in a cardboard box with straw and eggs and close the lid. You will then be able to transport them to the broody boxes easily. Let them sit in the cardboard box to regain their composure for an hour or two and then you can pop them quickly into the broody box onto the crock eggs already there. Alternatively move them when it is nearly dark.

Unless you have only one or two broodies it is best for you to get them off the nest every day. Try to do this at the same time, and tether them far enough apart so they cannot fight. To tether use a long thong or piece of string attached to the broody's leg with a sliding loop and on the other end a curtain ring dropped over a three foot high stick. Water and whole wheat only must be within reach, and the birds should be off the nest for about 20 minutes. Check that each one has defecated before you gently put her back. If not, you may have to help this proceedure by raising the hen to waist height and then dropping her on the ground. Several times may be necessary. As you are putting her back on the nest check that her feet are clean - hen manure will easily turn the eggs bad. If you want to use a system of putting the broodies in individual wire cages when taken off the nest, it is an alternative to tethering them but involves more equipment.

When the broodies have sat for a few days on the crock eggs and got used to whatever method you use for getting them off the nest each day, then is the time to set the eggs you want hatched.

Put the eggs under her in the evening - remember to take out the crock eggs - and after about an hour check she is covering them all properly. Take any away which are not covered. A large hen will cover 8-10 turkey eggs but if in doubt give her less. An odd number of eggs fits into a circle.

Don't forget to candle the eggs. See page 27.

A good broody will stay broody until she hatches off some youngsters. This may be after the 28 days or three months if you are juggling the eggs around to make the best use of the broodies. Don't be afraid of keeping a broody sitting on crock eggs until you are ready to set some hatching eggs. When you do set some clutches, try to set two or three at the same time. This means you will be able to amalgamate clutches after having discarded infertile or bad eggs and start one of the broodies off on another clutch. If a broody does become fierce and insits on pecking you she is only trying to protect her eggs. Offer your hand with your palm uppermost where the thicker skin will withstand the pecks better and turn your hand over once it is under the bird. Long sleeves are useful. Protective gloves are not really recommended as you can't feel what you are doing.

2. **Under a broody turkey**

Due to the comparatively short natural laying season of the turkeys some people would rather have the eggs off a turkey than for her to go broody as by the time she has sat for 28 days and then reared for another five weeks may well be the end of the laying season. Should you wish to use a turkey, they make excellent broodies if they can be allowed to settle. It is most important that the broody turkey is moved out of the breeding pen to avoid disturbance by the other turkeys. The same principles of management including moving her in the dark or in a box apply to the turkey as apply to the broody chicken. Her nestbox should be 18″ x 18″ x 24″ and she should cover 10-15 eggs. Remember to candle the eggs twice during the incubation period, once at 10 days and once at 20 days. (See below and next page)

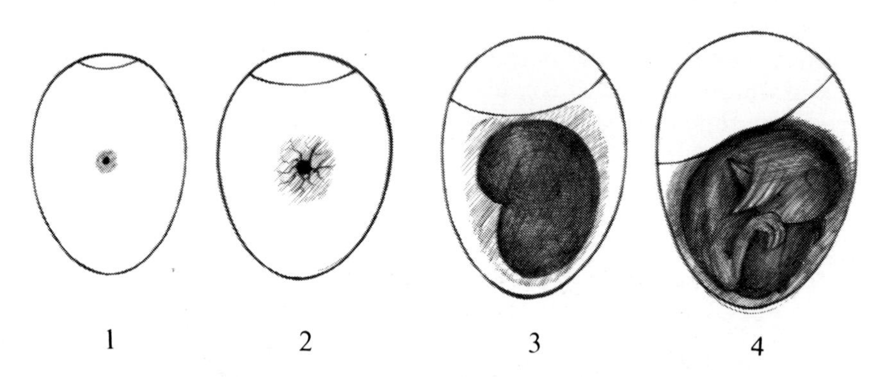

Stages in Incubation: 1: 5 days, 2: 10 days, 3: 18 days, 4: 26 days.

3. **Incubators**
(Incubation: 28 days for turkeys)

If you have an incubator or can borrow one it is imperative that the manufacturer's instructions are followed closely. Incubation is a complete science on its own, everyone achieving different levels of success with seemingly identical equipment. Recommended reading is Dr. Arthur Anderson Brown's "Incubation Book". It is important to stress that an incubator is only as good as the person operating it.

The main advantage of incubators over broodies is that they are available at any time of the year and they don't need feeding while they are not incubating.

What most manufacturers do not tell you is the importance of correct cleaning between hatches. Milton is the stuff to use, as the object is to sterilise. More poor hatches are obtained by bacteria left over from the previous hatch than any other cause.

How to candle eggs

Candling was originally done with the light of a candle for checking on embryo growth and is basically a concentrated source of light with which to see through the shell and into the eggs. Equipment available commercially ranges from a simple hand grip with a 10 watt bulb inside through ultra-violet "cool" lights and sophisticated machines which candle thousands of eggs automatically. A DIY version could consist of a three-sided wooden box with a household light fitting inside and a 1″ hole drilled in one side.

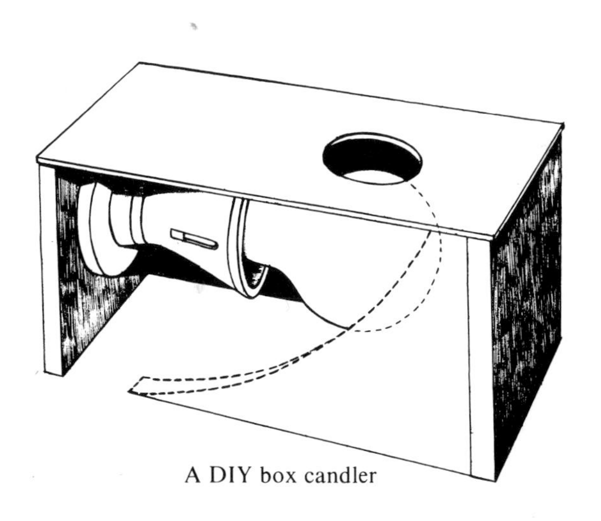

A DIY box candler

The hand held version is more flexible. The broad end of the egg is held to the light making sure that the light is pointing away from your eyes and that the room is as dark as possible. The air sac will be visible as a circular line at the broad end. The various stages of incubation are illustrated above. The infertiles - no dark areas - and the embryos which have died early on for one reason or another are very well illustrated in "The Incubation Book" mentioned above. Be especially careful if you can smell rotten eggs whether near the broody or in an incubator. If one explodes over you, you will be avoided by all humanity for a long time.

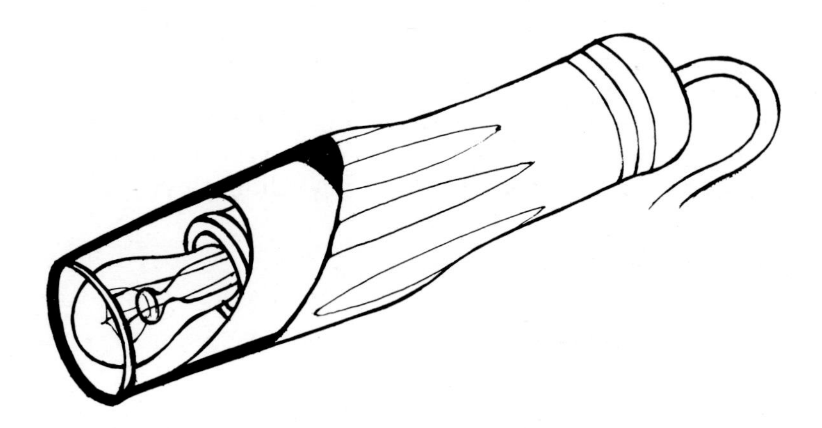

Hand held candler, quicker to use than the box version

Free range 12 week old coloured turkeys

Turkey eggs
(Domestic Fowl Trust)

Turkey chick at day old
(Domestic Fowl Trust)

Breeder turkey chick's - note the wing tags
(Domestic Fowl Trust)

Pied stag
(Domestic Fowl Trust)

Nebraskan stag
(Domestic Fowl Trust)

Norfolk Black stag
(Domestic Fowl Trust)

Buff stag
(Domestic Fowl Trust)

Slate and Lavender stags
(Domestic Fowl Trust)

Black Wing or Crimson Dawn stag
(Domestic Fowl Trust)

REARING

1. **Under a hen**

Once the chicks have hatched (it may take two days) remove all the shells and any eggs that did not make it. Turkey chicks can appear sleepy and wobbly when they are first hatched, but they soon strengthen up. Put turkey starter crumbs in a flat pan and a small drinker within reach of the hen, and before the brood is moved to a coop make sure the hen empties herself.

Depending on the weather and the time of year the coop and run can be indoors or outdoors. Size of coop and run should be approx. 5′ x 2′ x 2′. Put a few grains of wheat in with the crumbs for the hen to eat and after a few days when the chicks are feeding well change to a roll top feeder so that they can neither scratch the food around nor mess in it. If the coop is indoors make sure there is sufficient light and enough food, clean water daily, and take out the muck from the coop. The litter can be straw or shavings. If the coop is outdoors it can be moved on a daily basis and after four weeks the hen and chicks given their liberty if it is safe to do so. Turkey chicks are great insect stalkers and thrive on the daddy-long-legs in September. At 7-8 weeks the poults are independent, so take the hen away, letting the poults settle for a few days without her before moving them to larger quarters. This way you will avoid any setback due to an immediate double change of circumstances. Then continue as for Rearing page 33.

If using a turkey hen to hatch the chicks, the management is the same as above but the coop and run will have to be half as big again to allow for the greater size of the bird.

2. **Artificially**

At certain times of the year there will be a great demand on the turkey hatcheries. It is essential to put your order in early and with a reputable firm. This will ensure that you get the numbers you want, when you want and will reduce the chance of acquiring disease due to poor hatchery management. If you are hatching your own eggs in an incubator you must be aware of the disease risk from insufficient hygiene. A proprietory disinfectant especially for poultry is essential e.g. Antec Longlife 250S or Virkon S, and will prevent any build up of harmful organisms, unlike ordinary farm or garden disinfectants. Throughly disinfect the rearing room. Put plastic over the floor for protection from previous unknown use.

Location of rearing area: the rearing room must be at a continuous temperature of 70 degrees F (21 degrees C). This can be achieved by putting in false ceilings and walls made of plastic sheeting to contain the heat but there must also be ventilation. The rearing room must be vermin proof (rats, mice, starlings, sparrows) and kept reasonably quiet. Turkeys have higher blood pressure than other fowl and panic easily when very young. Refrain from sneezing or blowing your nose in this area for this reason.

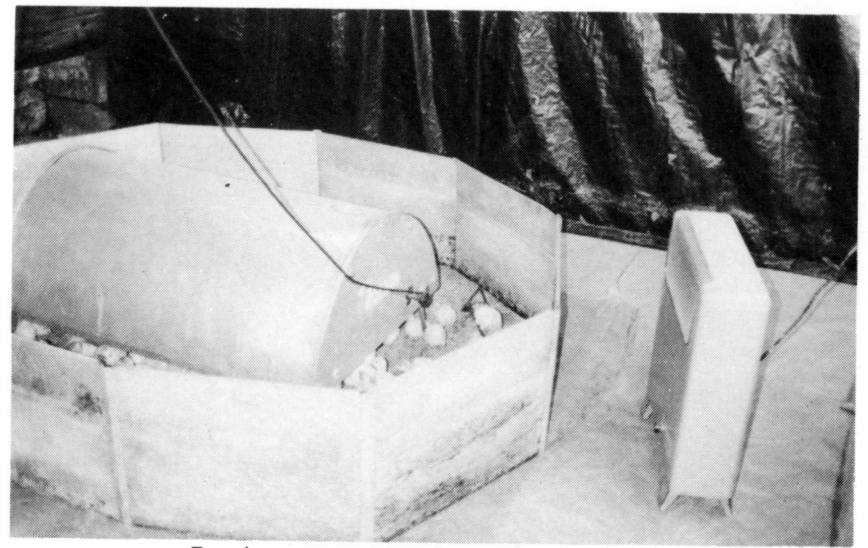

Rearing room with 4 days old turkey chicks

Equipment needed for 100 turkey chicks
8′ x 4′ sheet of hardboard, cut in half lengthways and joined by bulldog clips to form a circle 2′ high.
Brooder: your choice of:
gas brooder suitable for 100 turkey chicks
electric hen 2′ x 3′ See page 32.
3 infra-red dark emitters with shades (Salamander type 100 watt)
one 100 watt light bulb suspended near the brooder
2 half gallon plastic drinkers with red bases (birds have colour vision and are particularly attracted by red)
3 egg trays as preliminary feeders
4 2′ long roll top feeders (2″ per bird)
Shavings for the litter
Soluble vitamins
Turkey starter crumbs
Corrugated cardboard to put on top of the shavings for the first 3 days (stops the chicks eating the shavings)
An electric convector heater to maintain the heat in the rearing room
Fire extinguisher. Also check all electrical fittings and gas fittings.

Before the chicks arrive: set up the whole unit including soluble vitamins in the water and check for the temperature of the area. The temperature 2″ above the corrugated cardboard should be 98.6 degrees F (37 degrees C) directly under the brooder. Raise or lower the brooder to achieve this. If the chicks are too cold they will die quickly. If they are too hot they will also die quickly. Fill drinkers and position near the brooder. Scatter crumbs on the eggs trays and put near the brooder.

Day 1: Collect chicks from the railway station or hatchery as soon as possible. Get them to the rearing house quickly. Chick boxes are so designed that the chicks are kept warm by each other's body heat, but much depends on the outside temperature whether very high or very low. Get the chick boxes ready beside the hardboard surround and then count the chicks out of the boxes. Dip the beak of *each one* into the water, then the food and then put it under the brooder. Care taken at this stage will avoid troubles later on, as turkeys are reknowned for being slow to start feeding without some encouragement. If they do not feed, the yolk will last them for about three days and then they will die. Check the chicks every hour for the first critical day. If they are huddled together they are too cold, if all around the edges of the hardboard they are too hot. Once they strengthen up they should be scattered evenly over the area.
Day 2: Clean drinkers and refill. Add more food - slowly. Talk to the chicks. The best stockmen keep up a permanent monologue and always move slowly. Keep checking on them. Look under the brooder in case any have died in the night.
Day 3: Take up the corrugated cardboard - slowly. Cull any chicks which have splayed legs (gassing is the recommended method of culling for large numbers, but for practical purposes on small numbers, press the neck of the chick with your thumb onto a hard edge which severs the spinal cord instantly.) Clean and refill drinkers. Add more food. Talk to the chicks. Add a small amount of chick grit in two small pans. This helps the gizzard to develop.
Day 4: Take out drinkers and feeders. Add more shavings, slowly. If the shavings are getting scratched into the bases of the drinkers you will need to raise them about 1″ - an upside down feeding pan is ideal as it can be cleaned, unlike wood. Check under the brooder. Refill drinkers and add roll top feeders. Replace egg trays as well so that there is a gradual change over.
Day 5: Take drinkers and feeders out, add fresh shavings, slowly. Take egg trays away. Add more food to roll top feeders, pushing yesterday's food (if any) to one end and removing any shavings mixed with it. Clean and refill drinkers.
Day 6: Take drinkers and feeders out. Add fresh shavings. Clean and refill drinkers, add more fresh food as Day 5.
Day 7: as Day 6. Change 100 watt bulb to 25 watt bulb (still on for 24 hours). Increase drinkers to 3 and feeders to 6. Add more grit if necessary. Reduce temperature 2″ above litter under brooder to 91 degrees F (33 degrees C).

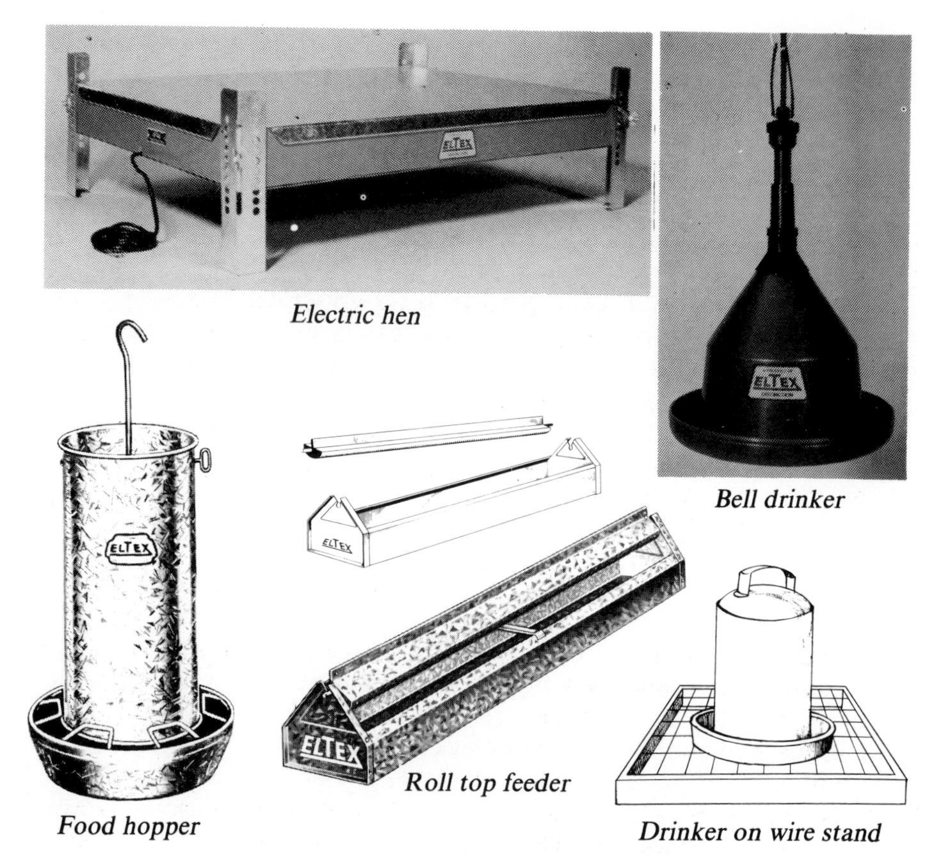

Electric hen

Bell drinker

Roll top feeder

Food hopper

Drinker on wire stand

Important to maintain in the first week: DRY litter
correct temperature
enought water and food
sufficient ventilation, no smell

Listen to the chicks - a change in noise will indicate a problem.
Avoid treading within the circle of hardboard as you will only add germs from other areas.

After Day 7 continue the daily routine of feeding, watering, providing fresh litter and checking on temperature.

Week 2: A wire stand for the drinkers will help with keeping the litter dry and thus avoiding disease build-up. Watch for a change in appetite - the first sign of disease is usually a reduction in food consumed. Reduce temperature 2″ above litter under brooder by 5 degrees F each week. Take out 25 watt bulb altogether so the chicks have natural day light. They seem to grow quicker if they have to sleep at night. The wing feathers are starting to grow and the chicks are becoming more adventurous. Expand the hardboard to give them more room.

Week 3: You may be able to remove the hardboard and give the chicks the full run of the rearing area if practical. Divisions will still have to be in the area to stop the chicks from straying as they are very inquisitive. Don't use bales of hay or straw as surrounds as the chicks have an uncanny knack of finding a crevice and getting stuck, only to be discovered when you move the bales later on, very dead. With the birds being dark at night you should not have any problems with feather pecking. If it starts, hang up two or three bunches of nettles in the rearing area about 4″ off the litter. This provides the birds with something to do (nettles fight back!). Feather pecking starts due to too much light, not enough water, not enough food, overcrowding, too hot, not enough ventilation, all of which are under *your* control. This is the reason why infra-red light heaters even the red ones are not used commercially, apart from being expensive to run.
Week 4: If the weather is reasonable and you are wanting your poults out at range they can be allowed limited access at this stage. Otherwise hang up more nettles.
Week 5: as Week 4. You may need to change to tube feeders, one 16″ diameter to 25 birds and an automatic watering system, one bell drinker to 50 birds.
The rearing for free range and intensive has been almost the same, so far. Week 6 is where it divides.
A. **Week 6 for Free Range turkeys:** at this time the chicks are called poults and are ready to be moved to their outside quarters. You will need 5 sq ft per bird in the range house which will take them up to slaughter weight. This is more space than the intensive birds, but when turkeys have been on range and, say, the weather is bad enough for them all to be in the house in the day time, they need the extra space to prevent bullying and feather pecking. If you have been rearing in batches of 100 and you want to increase the size of your group now is the time to do it. It is important that both groups are moved into the new quarters at the same time. This prevents one group establishing territory and then beating up the late arrivals. Use the same food hoppers and drinkers they have been used to in the rearing area so that they know where the food is obtained. If you want to change the system, do so gradually, leaving both sets functioning side by side for a day or so. This will avoid setbacks due to stress. Free range turkeys are never de-beaked or beak trimmed as it is unnecessary. The ideal range house is movable so that the immediate area round it does not get poached and sour, but if you are using a shed or stable, put slabs or slats around it to prevent mud. The birds should have direct access to a grassy paddock or orchard, preferably where turkeys have not been before. The building must be fox proof with clean litter and draught-free but with good ventilation positioned high up. It is at this stage that the

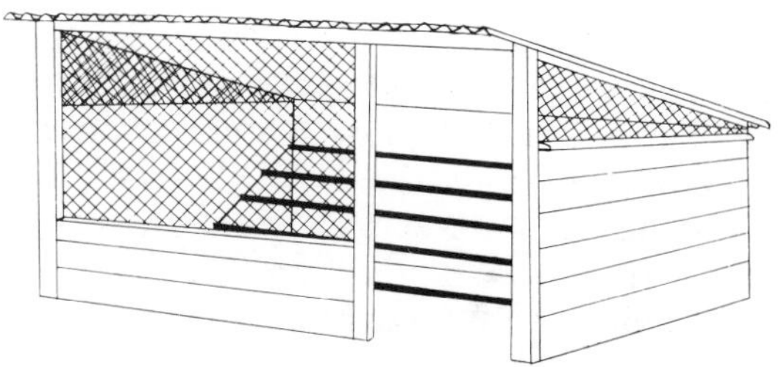

Free range house with door open

poults should go on to a grower or rearer pellet. Mix the new food with the starter crumbs for a day or two so again, there is a gradual change over. If you are buying in poults at this stage make sure the corners of the shed have cardboard in them to round them off as you will not know if the poults have been used to the dark and may try and smother each other in their fright. If possible hang a 25 watt bulb in the range shed so they are less frightened by so many strange things. Perches of 2″ x 2″ or 2″ x 3″ can be put in the range shed from week 6, allowing 18″ space per bird.

Keep the poults fenced in with 4′ netting for a week so they get their bearings. The water fonts can be moved outside. Let them range fully after the eigth week. Up to 20% of their daily consumption of food will be grass from this time on and they will search out clover and other herbs such as plantain. They love thistles and can be used as organic weed killers. They will roam quite a distance, always in a pack, probably getting into mischief with their innate curiosity. It is important to drive them into the safety of the range house at night as if the weather is warm they will want to roost outside. Turkeys are very stupid with foxes as curiosity will make them advance towards one.

A dose of anti-blackhead drug in the water may be necessary when they first go out to range. This assumes there is none in the feed. We are not in favour of using drugs in the feed as a matter of course as they can become an excuse for poor management. With the shift in emphasis towards natural or organic feeding of birds and animals for meat it is important to realise that they can be reared without drugs of any kind - this method takes a higher standard of management to be done successfully. (Diseases, see page 50.)

Feeding: 6-10 weeks on turkey grower pellets
10-18 weeks on ⅔ grower, ⅓ whole wheat
18 weeks onwards ⅓ grower, ⅔ whole wheat
} plus ad lib mixed grit

Free range with fox-proof fence: this method is much less labour intensive as the birds do not have to be let out or shut in and the range shelter can be moved on a regular basis. (See page 19.)

B. **Week 6 onwards for Intensively reared turkeys:** the chicks are now called poults and are ready to be moved to larger indoor quarters. At this stage most people de-beak or beak trim the birds to avoid cannibalism. One third of the top beak is removed and cauterized in one operation with a machine. It must be carried out by a skilled operator. If birds are de-beaked or beak trimmed deeper feed troughs and deeper water drinkers must be provided to compensate.

Beak trimming: too much, just right, too little

This is the time to make a larger group, when they all go into new quarters. You cannot add any more at a later date as they will be attacked - you may think that all white turkeys look the same, but the turkeys do not think so. It is as well to leave a light on all night so they can find their way to the feed and water until they settle down, and add vitamins to the water for 3 days. Perches are not normally provided for intensive systems so the litter has to be kept dry to avoid soiling of the birds. (You can use straw but be aware of the danger from mould spores -aspergillosis). Shavings would need to be 2″ - 3″ thick to begin with, more being added at intervals. Space needed is 3 sq ft per bird average weight. If you are rearing hens and stags separately, hens will need 3 sq ft per bird and stags 4½ sq ft per bird. Turkeys can be reared as mixed sexes but there is a danger of the stags treading the hens and damaging them, overcome by pulling out the stags as they get to that stage for early slaughter. The poults go onto a grower or rearer pellet at Week 6, but change it over gradually by mixing it in with the crumbs to avoid stress and/or upset in the birds' digestive system.

The feed is put in hoppers, one 16″ diameter one to 25 birds. The hoppers are suspended so that the pan is level with the backs of the birds. Water is more convenient if it is in automatic drinkers but do check several times a day that the pipes are not clogged or the things are overflowing -wet litter is the start of trouble.

Any type of shed or pole barn can be used for turkey rearing providing there is sufficient ventilation, security from foxes and other vermin, electricity including lighting for inspecting the birds, food, water. A 40′ x 20′ shed will accommodate 250 turkeys to slaughter weight (3 sq ft/bird). It is not recommended to have groups larger than this.

Any suitable building can be used

The same barn, from the inside

It may be useful to rear a few guinea fowl with the turkeys. Guinea fowl are always rushing about and this helps to prevent the turkeys panicking at a sudden noise. Guinea fowl are susceptible to some drugs, so check what is in the feed. Guineas will act as watchdogs and sound the alarm if there is something amiss.

Warning: certain anti-coccidials can kill adult turkeys such as the ionophore Monesin. ALWAYS READ THE LABEL ON THE BAG.

Finishing: this is normally the period of about two weeks before slaughter. It includes any withdrawal period necessary if drugs have been used in the food. How do you know when a turkey is 'finished'? It is most unlikely that all the birds in a group will have reached the same stage at the same time even if they have been segregated by sex. 22-24 weeks of age is average, some commercials are quicker. Hens are usually ready a couple of weeks before the stags. The best way to determine which birds are finished is to catch them individually. The pin or immature feathers should be through the skin. Check on the amount of fat deposited under the skin. Gently pinch a fold of skin on the breast, near the base of the wing. A well fattened bird will have thick, cream coloured skin. A bird which is not ready will have thin, semi-transparent skin which is often reddish. Be *very* careful when handling the birds as they bruise easily which will downgrade the carcase. See page 7 and 39.

BATCH OR PEN RECORD

QUANTITY .... **TYPE** .... **SEX** ....

MONTH	TEMP MAX	TEMP MIN	DEATHS	CAUSES	WATER CONSUMED	FOOD CONSUMED	MEDICATION	SAMPLE WEIGHTS
DAY 1								
2								
3								
4								
5								
6								
7								
8								
9								
10								
11								
12								
13								
14								

Rearing turkeys indoors intensively: Feed consumption for 100 birds

Type of feed	***Age in weeks***	***No. of 25Kg bags***	***Protein***
Turkey starter	0-4	6	28%
Turkey rearer	4-8	20	24%
Turkey grower	8-16	60	20%
Turkey finisher	16 +	14 bags per week	16%

Water consumption of growing turkeys: per 100 birds

Week 1	1 gall.
Week 2	2
Week 3	3
Week 4	4
Week 5	5
Week 6	6
Week 7	8
Week 8	9
Week 9	11.5
Week 10	13
Week 11	15
Week 12	16
Week 13	17
Week 14	18
Week 15	18
Week 16	18
Week 17	18
Week 18	18
Week 19	18
Week 20	18

It should be noted that the higher the temperature where the birds are, the more they will drink.

Performance Standards (average)

Age in weeks	4	8	12	16	20	24	28
Stag liveweight (lb)	1.7	5.5	11.9	18.5	24.6	30.2	34.1
Hen liveweight (lb)	1.1	4.4	8.8	13.2	16.5	18.7	—

Preparation of turkeys for killing

Starving

The birds must be starved for 12 hours before they are killed. Withold grain for a 12 hour period before that as grain takes longer to get through the system. The birds must have access to water. Starving the birds for 12 hours ensures that the gut is empty which prevents degeneration and discolouring of the carcase.

Catching

Turkeys bruise very easily so it is most important to handle them with care. Do not let them trample each other in their efforts to get away from you. It is useful to have a small holding pen into which you can quietly drive some of the birds. Putting gorse into the corners of a big pen will prevent some trampling damage. Quietly and slowly reach down and take hold of both shanks of the bird. Do not let the breast thump to the floor as this will bruise it. Hold the legs in one hand and gently lift the bird, tucking it under your arm and holding the wings down securely between your arm and your body. You do not need to be bruised by the turkey, either, as a clout from a wing is something best not repeated. For best results, catching and killing wants to be done in small batches to allow the minimum of stress to the birds. The meat from stressed birds is of lower quality.

See Code of Practice page 45.

Killing:

Broomstick: the head of the bird is placed under a broomstick, an assistant stands on both sides of the broomstick and the body of the turkey is jerked upwards to dislocate its neck. Needs a certain amount of brute strength on the bigger birds.

Humane despatcher: this is a device for severing the spinal column without breaking the skin. It has the advantage that it is instant and the job has been done quickly and cleanly. It also makes a gap for the blood to drain into.

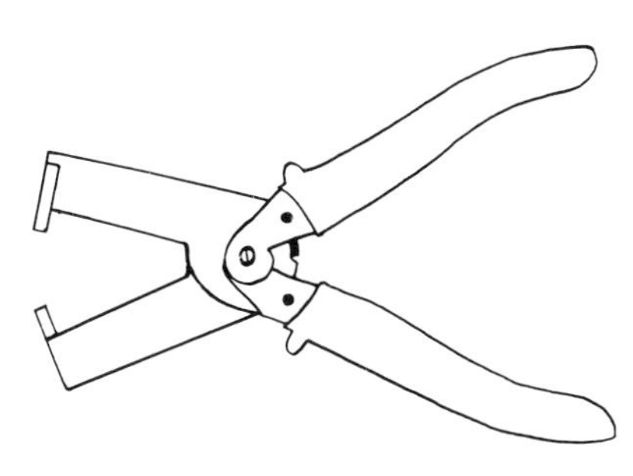

Semark pliers. A recently patented humane killer which works by severing the windpipe and dislocating the neck vertebrae at the same time.

Airgun: Useful for a few birds and again, instantaneous as the muzzle of the airgun is placed at the back of the head of the turkey, the legs being held in the other hand. It does not allow for the correct bleeding, so the jugular vein should be cut as well.

Whatever method you use for killing turkeys, they will flap their wings. Be careful that the wings do not hit anything as this will bruise them. Hang the birds by their legs in shackles or by rope.

Killing a turkey with an airgun

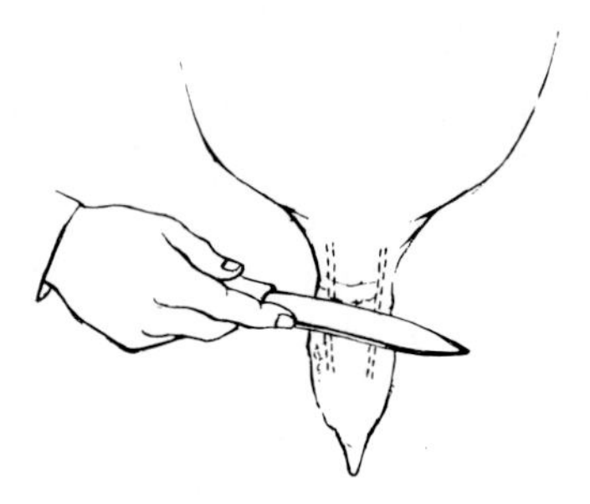

Bleeding a turkey - the jugular veins are shown as dotted lines

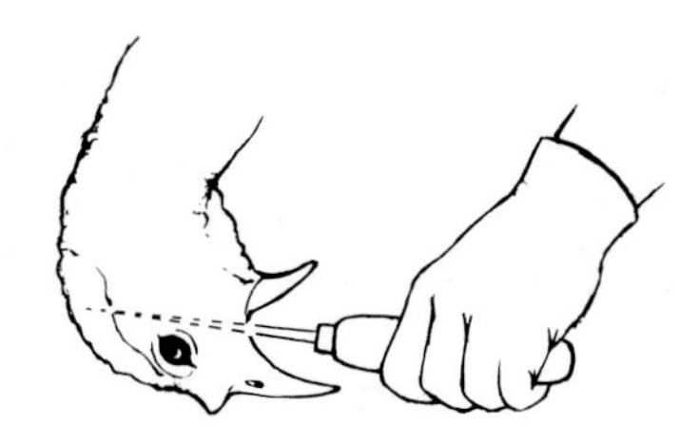

Sticking a turkey

Bleeding: The blood needs to drain from the carcase of birds which are to be hung or cold-stored. This increases the keeping qualities. The gap in the neck if the humane despatcher has been used will suffice, but otherwise the veins will have to be cut and a cup fitted onto the turkeys head to catch the blood - can be rather messy.

Sticking: It is said that if the turkey's brain is stuck with a knife in the back portion the feathers come out easier. This has already been achieved if the airgun method has been used. See diagram. It is important to hold the head of the bird correctly to avoid cutting yourself.

Plucking: Best done as soon after killing as possible as the feathers are easier to remove if the bird is still warm. ***Hand Plucking*** does give the best finish but it is labour intensive and there seem to be fewer people who are prepared to learn how to do it. If you are going to pluck all your turkeys yourself, spread the operation over several days as each bird can take an hour for a novice, about 20 minutes for an experienced plucker. You will require something suitable to hang the bird up by, a rope or a wire shackle, with the legs spread, a plastic apron, a large cardboard box for the feathers, a chair and a radio. There is no denying that either company or a radio helps the operation to be more enjoyable. Start plucking near the tail on the back. Hold a small bunch of feathers in one hand and put the fingers of the other hand on the skin at the base of the feathers. Jerk the feathers quickly and they will come away easily. The amount of jerk and the angle of pull will come with practice. It is not difficult, but care must be taken not to tear the skin. If you start on the back, any small tears are going to be less noticeable until you get into your stride. Also, any blood remaining in the carcase if very recently killed may well up into the feather follicles. This again will be less noticeable on the back. The blood does not take long to drain (2 - 3 minutes). You will notice that the feathers are arranged in patterns, or tracts, some areas being almost feather free. Keeping to a routine of back, down to neck, then tail, wings, legs and breast feathers will speed up the process. Tail and wing feathers are usually removed with the help of pliers. Fine hairs will be left after the feathers have been removed. These will be singed off later. Any small stubs or pin feathers can be removed with a blunt-bladed knife held to the thumb.

There is a small demand for coloured turkey feathers for craftwork, so if you have found a market for these, keep them separate, making sure they are clean.

Machine Plucking: two sorts:

1. **Dry plucking:** this machine has revolving plates or wheels to which the bird is held and rotated slowly. A fan sucks the feathers up and away into a bag. It speeds up the operation to a level of about 5 minutes per bird, but the tail and wing feathers still have to be hand done. These machines do a good job and can be worked by unskilled people.

2. **Wet plucking:** this is more complicated as the bird has to be semi-scalded. The water must be 125-130 degrees F, if it is colder the feathers will not be lifted, if it is hotter, the skin will be reddened thus downgrading the carcase. A thermostatic urn of about 30 gallons will be the right size. Time held in the water is also important, about 30 seconds. The bird is then held against rotating rubber fingers which not only take the feathers off but one layer of skin as well. If the bird is not immediately gutted, the skin must be kept moist otherwise it will discolour. Care must be taken that the operator does not get scalded.

Wax plucking: the bird is dipped in hot paraffin wax (125-130 degrees F), left to cool for 15 to 30 minutes and then the wax is removed. This takes all the feathers and the hairs with it and even removes the stubs. The wax can be reused by melting and straining.

If the birds are to be sold New York Dressed or Longlegged, this means they are plucked but not gutted with clean feet.

Cooling: it is important that the birds are cooled quickly, down to about 32 degrees F to inhibit the growth of bacteria. They should not freeze, but the heat removed from inside the birds down to 35 degrees F. A temperature controlled area is ideal where the birds should be hung, with enough space around for the air to circulate freely. Press the vent area to expel any waste material before hanging. The turkeys, particularly free range ones, should stay in the cool room for a week ensuring that it is fly proof. A stone or brick building, suitably painted, vermin proof, cleaned, will probably be cool enough in an English winter, but be aware of warm spells which could raise the temperature high enough to cause rapid degeneration of the carcase.

If you are selling the birds Longlegged then they can go at any time after they are cooled and singed. They must be labelled with your name and address, the date and weight of the bird.

Singeing: when the birds are ready for gutting they can be quickly singed with a hand held gas torch. Do not scorch the skin.

Evisceration or gutting

It is vital that conditions are kept as hygienic as possible. Do not use wooden surfaces as these cannot be cleaned. Melamine is acceptable, stainless steel is the best.

It is best to start by cutting the skin on the front of the shanks to expose the tendons. These can be removed by looping them over a hook and pulling. This will tenderise the legs. Cut through the hock joint, leaving a flap of skin on the back of the joint to prevent the skin shrinking up the leg during cooking.

Cut the skin around the neck near the head and then cut the head off. Cut the skin of the neck down the back to between the shoulder blades. Cut the neck off between the shoulder blades using heavy shears. The gullet, crop and wind pipe can then be carefully removed, cutting close to the body cavity as possible. This leaves a flap of skin which is folded under the bird to keep the juices in when cooking and to provide a cavity for the stuffing if wanted. Cut off the tips of the wings. Then make a cut between the vent and the parson's nose, push a finger into the cavity and loop the intestine round the finger. Then cut around the vent, leaving the vent attached to the end of the intestine. Make the cut slightly larger so you can get two fingers into the body cavity. The gizzard will be felt, about egg size, pull on this carefully and most of the organs should come out. Separate the heart, the liver, don't break the gall bladder which is green as it will taint it, neck and gizzard, the lining of which is easily removed after cutting the gizzard lengthways, as all these constitute the giblets. Make sure the body cavity is empty before washing it out with cold water. Wash outside the bird as well. Hang the bird up to drip. Wash the giblets and then wrap them in cellophane. Pat dry with kitchen paper (or disposable cloth) the rest of the turkey. Put the giblets inside the body cavity. It is enough to keep the legs together with a rubber band as if you truss the bird properly and the customer wants to stuff it, all the trussing will have to be undone.

The turkey is now ready to be placed in a large cellophane bag and the air squeezed out and the bag tied securely. The bird must be labelled with your name and address, the date and the weight of the bird.

The turkey can now be sold fresh or quick-frozen for selling at a later date.

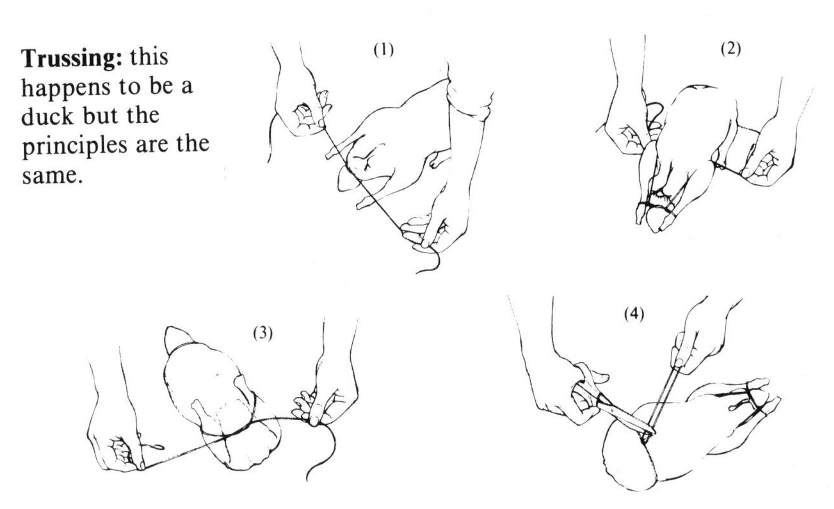

Trussing: this happens to be a duck but the principles are the same.

Killing out percentages

Live Weight	Oven ready *(75% of Live Weight)*	Live Weight	Oven ready *(75% of Live Weight)*	Live Weight	Oven ready *(75% of Live Weight)*
10lb	7lb 8oz	17lb	12lb 12oz	24lb	18lb
11lb	8lb 4oz	18lb	13lb 8oz	25lb	18lb 12oz
12lb	9lb	19lb	14lb 4oz	30lb	22lb 8oz
13lb	9lb 12oz	20lb	15lb	35lb	26lb 4oz
14lb	10lb 8oz	21lb	15lb 12oz	40lb	30lb
15lb	11lb 4oz	22lb	16lb 8oz		
16lb	12lb	23lb	17lb 4oz		

MARKETING AND REGULATIONS

It is essential to organise the sale of your birds before you buy or hatch them. This book is aimed at the smaller producer, 1-1000 birds. If you have no experience in rearing turkeys and lack capital for housing and equipment, go for the person to person market and start with a few -maximum 25 birds. Far better to do too few and put people on the waiting list for next year than be left with too many and no market. Free range or barn reared is probably the easiest to begin with. Put a sign at your gate and take orders early. Get people to leave a deposit, which not only protects you from the annoying ones who say they have been fixed up elsewhere at the last moment, but gives you something towards the feed bills. Ensure that your customers are satisfied, ask their opinion on the quality and presentation of the meat. Do they want small birds in the 8-10lb range or something rather larger? Your birds have got to be better by taste, presentation and delivery than anyone else's. There is no finer recommendation than by mouthwatering word of mouth.

The smaller producer can find markets in local restaurants, hotels, clubs, pubs, old people's homes, in fact all end users. If you sell to butchers you will lose on the price but it may be more convenient to have just one outlet.

Advertising can be done in various ways - lineage in your local newspaper, a sign at your gate, leaflets put through doors, orders taken at the pub, whichever method you choose do not lose a chance to tell people about your birds: what they are fed on (additive free?), how they are housed (free range?), and how good and tasty they are - you have of course tried one so you know at first hand.

Whether you decide to sell your turkeys New York Dressed or eviscerated is a personal choice, but either way you are by law obliged to label the bird with your name and address. An eviscerated bird must be suitably wrapped, preferably in a clear plastic bag. Labels can be tie on or stick on. Consider having special stick on ones done with your name and farm or logo with space for weights and the date which can also be used for guinea fowl, chickens, ducks etc. Danro Ltd. will design your very own label at modest cost.

When you are a little more established, try a small booklet attached to each bird giving details of cooking, various types of stuffing, suggestions for the use of cold turkey meat etc. Attention to detail is vital.

REGULATIONS

Extracts from the NFU Code of Practice for on-farm slaughter and marketing of Poultry.

"A

INTRODUCTION

This Code of Practice is designed for producers growing and marketing their own(1) poultry(2) who are exempt from the Poultry Meat (Hygiene) Regulations 1976 as amended, which implement EC Directive 71/118.

All producers so exempt must, however, comply with the Food Hygiene (General) Regulations 1970. This Code sets out your legal obligations under these 1970 Regulations and indicates how, in practical terms, these may best be met. We would stress that the suggestion under the headings "Practical Implementation" are not legal requirements and as many Local Authorities hold differing views we would strongly recommend that you take advice on aspects of this Code from your local Environmental Health Officer, your local N.F.U. Secretary or Regional Poultry Secretary, and A.D.A.S. Poultry Adviser, particularly before investing capital in buildings or equipment.

When introducing the exemptions to the Poultry Meat (Hygiene) Regulations 1976, which allowed the trade in Traditional Farm Fresh poultry to continue, the then Minister of Agriculture made it perfectly clear that these would "be reviewed in due course, in the light of developments". If the traditional fresh trade is to continue it is essential that producers ensure that the preparation of their poultry for sale is at least to the standard required by the Food Hygiene (General) Regulations 1970. The penalties for not abiding by the Regulations can be severe.

The basic principle behind all food hygiene, is the avoidance of cross-contamination and the possibility of subsequent food poisoning. In relation to poultry, each step in the slaughter and preparation process should be kept separate and such waste as feathers, and blood and offal where applicable, should be regularly removed and leave the building in a different direction from the flow of birds. This is illustrated in the diagram (Page 46). Obviously, personal hygiene, clean equipment and buildings are essential.

(1) These exemptions apply only to your own-produced poultry a "Producer" being defined in this context as one who sells poultry meat derived from poultry which has been kept alive on his premises for at least 21 days prior to slaughter (See part B for restrictions on sales).

(2) Defined as domestic fowls, turkeys, guinea fowl, ducks and geese in the Poultry Meat (Hygiene) Regulations 1976. Welfare provisions under the Slaughter of Poultry Act 1967, as amended, also cover quail."

"As well as the Food and Hygiene (General) Regs 1970, the producer should be aware of the general provisions of the Food Act 1984 under which it is an offence to sell food for human consumption which may be injurious to health or is not of the nature, substance or quality demanded by the purchaser.

Whatever the size and type of enterprise, it is of vital importance that the buildings, equipment and procedures followed accord with the principles of good hygiene and that statutory hygiene requirements are observed."

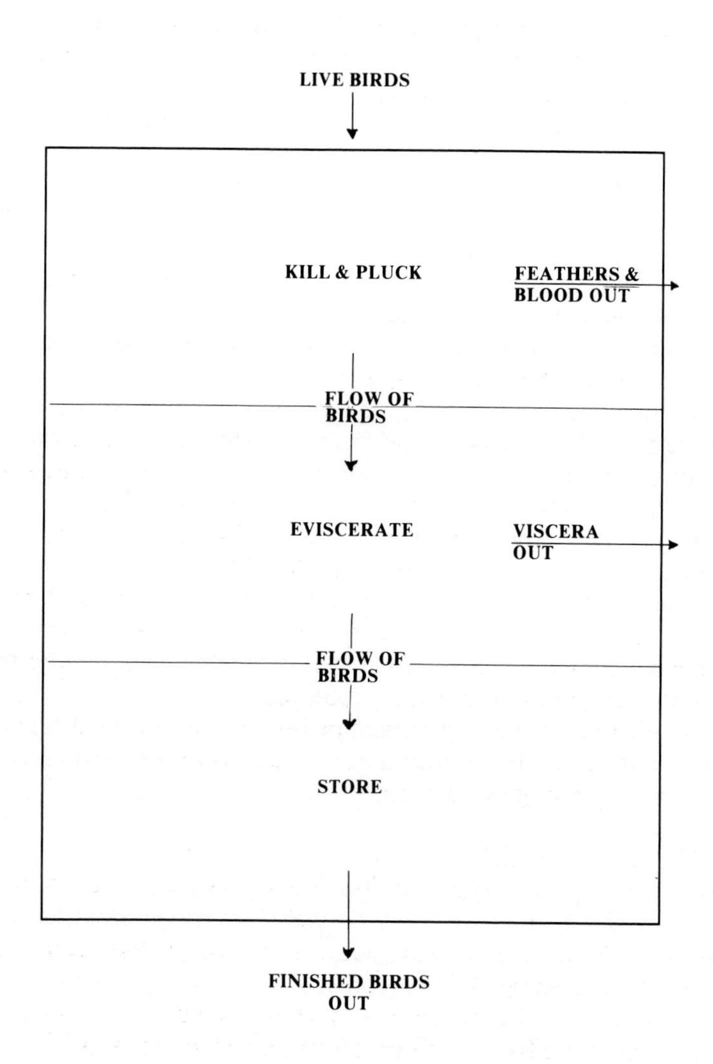

"B

EXCLUSIONS FROM THE POULTRY MEAT (HYGIENE) REGULATIONS 1976

These Regulations implement EC Directive 71/118, as amended, in England and Wales, and were the first to specifically cover the slaughter of poultry. As a producer-marketer you are exempt from the 1976 Regulations and do not have to register exept in respect of the Slaughter of Poultry Act

provided:-

(a) You sell your own produced poultry meat, which can be **wet** or **dry plucked, eviscerated or uneviscerated** (but see (c) below)

- **direct to the final consumer irrespective of the place of sale** except that itinerant sales and sales by mail order are prohibited and sales at markets are restricted as below. You may be able to deliver to your customer provided the actual sale has taken place as above;
- **direct to the final customer at markets** in your Local Authority's area or a neighbouring locality;
- **to retailers in your Local Authority's area or a neighbouring L.A.** (eg butchers, not wholesalers) for direct resale to the final consumer; there is no restriction on the place of sale by the retailer to the final consumer.

"The final consumer" means not only the housewife but also any person who buys poultry meat for consumption on his own premises or on premises under his management or control, e.g. hotels, cafes, restaurants, schools or any other catering establishment.

(b) You sell your own produced **dry plucked, whole bodied,** birds, slaughtered on your own premises. In this instance, there is no restriction as to type of outlet, buyer or locality, and such birds may be sold to whoever or wherever you like. The bird **must** however, have a label attached giving the name and address of the premises where slaughter and plucking took place.

(c) You sell **poultry meat portions or boned poultry meat** direct to the final consumer from premises, or adjacent premises, where the cutting or boning takes place.

IMPORTANT NOTES

(a) These exemptions apply to your own-produced birds, a 'producer' being defined in this context as one who sells poultry meat derived from poultry which **he has kept alive on his premises for at least 21 days prior to slaughter.**

(b) It should also be remembered that under the Food Act 1984 Environmental Health Officers have powers of entry at all reasonable times."

EXHIBITION OF TURKEYS

Although in the last few years there has been a handful of turkeys at the major shows, very few people keep turkeys to show. This is a pity as the stags can display wonderfully, helping to educate people, and with all the colour variations around it is also great fun. Due to the size and strength of turkeys, handling them needs some practice, see page

Turkeys used for showing are usually the coloured vatieties as white is the most difficult to keep clean, almost always needing to be washed. Only very early hatched stags will be mature enough to show in their first year, but hens will be, albeit lacking the appeal of the strutting stags.

The main problem is penning up birds from the end of their moult, normally August/September, and keeping them pristine until November/December when the major shows occur in England. Trying to show a turkey in high summer is virtually impossible due to the age of the feathers - nothing can beat a new feather for lustre and form. As mentioned elsewhere they enjoy scrapping amongst themselves which produces scarring and broken feathers. Tail feathers quickly become ragged when rubbed against wire, so your plywood divisions in your breeding house are ideal for autumn penning. Turkeys should not be shown with their wings clipped.

Entries for shows usually close 6 weeks before the show, so get your entry in on the correct form in plenty of time. The Show Secretary will furnish you with an entry form and a schedule of classes. (At least two entered will ensure they have company).

Unless very tame, most turkeys will benefit from a bit of pen training so that they will be relaxed and show off to the judge and not cower in a corner. An easy way to do this is to make a 4′ square out of hurdles or wood (the turkey must be able to see at least out of the front), placed near the back door where there are people passing and put the chosen bird in for a few hours each day a week before the show. He will soon settle down and should display whenever he sees anyone. The hens also benefit from this training, particularly if spoilt with titbits such as pears or raisins.

A good de-lousing should be done about 2 weeks before the show. Washing is usually unnecessary on the coloured birds, but any washing should be done a week before the show to let the feathers regain their shine. Use a soft soap and tepid water and rinse well. If the legs are very dirty rub some Swarfega in and leave for a day or two to get under the scales, then scrub with a nailbrush. A little Vaseline on the legs and beaks gives the finishing touch just before they are crated.

Transporting them to the show should not undo all your hard work by crates being too cramped or dirty. Don't however, do as we did and build three beautiful crates which were so large only two of them would fit in our trailer. The other point is not to make the crates too heavy - remember, the bird inside may weigh up to 56lbs.

A crate suitable for transporting turkeys. Approx. dimensions 30″ x 30″ x 36″ high. A Narragansett hen is in the crate.

Depending on the length of show, take a drinker (a large margarine tub with wire threaded through one side to anchor it to the pen) and enough food to last the show. A watering can is useful if you have entered several birds, but put your name clearly on it as they have a habit of walking. When you arrive at the show make sure you have the correct pen number and then put your birds in the right pens, making sure there is straw or shavings in there first, usually provided by the show. If your crates have been well built there should be little or no re-arranging of tail feathers to do.

After the show the birds will need a good wing-stretch and they may also lose weight due to the stress of travelling, so cosset them a bit when you get home. Again, de-louse in case any of any extras picked up at the show.

It is a good idea to display your prize cards and rosettes somewhere at your point of sale i.e. where your customers can see them, so that the customer can be impressed by your winnings. This also has the effect of re-inforcing the prices of your breeding birds when people are buying into a winning strain.

DISEASES AND AILMENTS

There are some diseases specific to turkeys, or more commonly found in them. With the swing towards additive free meat, turkey feeds are now available without drugs or growth promoters in. If a bird is sick then it can be treated with the correct drug. Natural immunity is possible, if not desirable.

Drugs must never become a substitute for good management.

Whatever diseases or ailments you treat you must by law keep a record of it. Withdrawal periods must be adhered to before slaughter.

DISEASES AND AILMENTS

SYMPTOMS	NAME	CAUSE	TREATMENT	BIRD SPECIES AFFECTED
Listless, head sunk into neck. White diarrohea, sometimes blood in droppings	Coccidiosis	Coccidia parasite.	1 teaspoonful Sulphamex in ½ gall. water for 5 days. Renew if consumed. Make no other water available	chickens, turkeys, peafowl, pheasants, guinea fowl, quail.
Listless, head sunk in neck. Yellow diarrohea.	Blackhead	Parasite carried by Heterakis worm.	1 sachet Emtryl to 1 gall. water in screw top jar. Give for 5 days. Renew after 3 days if not all consumed. Make no other water available.	chickens, turkeys, peafowl, pheasants, quail guinea fowl.
Listless, green diarrohea. Gaping in pheasants. Loss of weight in waterfowl.	Worms.	Up to 6 different species of worm inhabiting different internal parts	Mebenvet mixed into feed in trough, 1 tablespoon to 2 lb feed. Geese and ducks 3 days, all else 7 days.	chickens, ducks, geese turkeys, peafowl, quail, guinea fowl.
Excessive scratching, visible fleas around vent. Redness around vent. Sometimes colonies of eggs on base of feathers. White dust around perch fittings - mites. Lassitude. Infertility.	Fleas or mites.	4 types of flea. 2 types of mite.	Dust with flea powder particularly around vent and under wings. About 1 oz per bird. Spray housing especially around perch fixings where red and white mite live and feed on birds at night, with Duramitex. Put flea powder in nest boxes.	All birds.
Sneezing, discharge from nostrils, foam in corner of eye. Swollen sinus in turkeys. Sweet, sickly smell.	Mycoplasma (cold)	Bacteria	One injection of ½ ml. per bird in breast muscle of Tylan 200. 1 ml. for very large birds e.g. turkeys. Repeat only in very bad cases 3 days after first injection. Mild cases, Tylan soluble in water.	chickens, turkeys, peafowl, pheasants

SYMPTOMS	NAME	CAUSE	TREATMENT	BIRD
Blood	Wound	Feather-pecking due to over-crowding. Accidental cut.	Terramycin Gentian Violet spray on area and isolate until healed.	Young Stock or any other birds.
Raised, encrusted scales on legs.	Scaly Leg	Mite, burrowing under.	Brush surgical spirit on affected legs with small paintbrush twice, 5 days apart. Do not pull off crusts.	Any bird.
Brown diarrohea, slow growth, poor feathering in young stock, affected by the cold, several deaths overnight.	Enteritis	Escherichia coli (E. coli) bacteria, usually due to poor ventilation, dirty conditions.	1 measure per gall. water changed every 24 hours of Terramycin in water for 3 days. If that doesn't work (bacteria immune?) use Framomycin, 1 measure per gall. water for 5 days.	Young, stock, of chickens, ducks, geese, turkeys, peafowl, pheasants, quail.
Purple comb, when normally bright red.	Heart disease	Age or deformity	No treatment	chickens
Round swelling on underside of foot	Bumble foot	Injury first, then infection.	Can be surgically removed	chickens, pheasants. turkeys, guinea fowl.
Top part of beak grown much longer than bottom.	Overgrown beak	Deformity - beak should meet exactly	Trim back to level with lower portion with sharp scissors. Careful not to cut the quick.	All birds.
Sides of females bleeding or bare of feathers	Bareback.	Sharp, long spurs of males.	Trim with hacksaw, careful not to cut the quick. File smooth and rounded	All birds, which have spurs.
Unusual behaviour	Stress	Unusual disturbance or major changes - adding new stock	Tablespoon of vitamin powder in 1 gall. water for 5 days.	Any bird. Stress can cause dormant illness to take over the body.
Lameness	Injury, or something wrong internally.	Possibly a tumour	Keep quiet and isolated. If an injury it should heal. If a tumour it will get gradually worse. No treatment.	Any bird.
Wasting away but still feeding.	Avian tuberculosis	Bacteria	No treatment - carried by wild birds. Natural immunity possible.	All birds.

SPEED is essential.
A postmortem will establish cause of death and possible treatment of other birds.
ONE medicine at any one time.
Most medicines are only obtainable through a vet. Contact The Domestic Fowl Trust for an up to date list of poultry vets in your area. (The DFT is licensed to sell wormers and certain veterinary products).
Wash hands after handling medicines.
Do not eat eggs or birds when medicines are being given nor for a week afterwards or follow the withdrawal instructions on the label.

Blackhead: **cause** - parasite in the liver and caeca (blind gut). Rarely does the head turn black.
Symptoms: yellow droppings; mopey, quiet birds, not interested in food. Sulphurous smell to droppings. Poults will die within 24 hours if not treated, adults 2-4 days, so act **quickly.**
Treatment: Emtryl in the water. Make no other water available. It may be necessary to treat the whole flock. The birds recover very quickly.
Prevention: a certain amount of immunity is aquired by free range birds. The parasite spends part of its life cycle in the *Heterakis* worm which lives in the caeca or blind gut of both turkeys and chickens. Worming (using Mebenvet) can reduce the incidence of Blackhead.
Coccidiosis: **Cause:** Parasite in the gut.
Symptoms: Young birds, which are most susceptible, look cold, mopey, off their food, whitish or bloody droppings. More of a danger after a spell of wet weather and in late summer on free range.
Treatment: anti-coccidials in the feed are supposed to prevent infection but they are not always effective. When an outbreak is confirmed an anti-coccidial may be added to the water such as Sulphamex.
Prevention: natural immunity is acquired, high quality feed helps as does keeping the ground/litter dry.
Omphalitis: **cause:** poor hatchery hygiene.
Symptoms: in day old chicks, this is a navel infection, the birds either die or do poorly and there is a nasty smell.
Treatment: cull infected birds.
Prevention: only buy in from reputable sources.
E. coli: **cause:** bacteria normally present in the gut which multiply in dirty conditions and affect stressed birds, particularly young ones.
Symptoms: brown diarrhea, hunched appearance, slow growth, a few dead each day, a strong sweetish smell.
Treatment: throughly clean rearing area and disinfectant with Antec 250S. Wood is a harbourer, so spread builders grade plastic as a floor covering and up the sides for 12″. Disinfect all feeders, drinkers, the brooder, anything the chicks come into contact with. Administer a broad spectrum antibiotic in the drinking water. Plain yoghurt helps restore the correct gut flora.
Prevention: good hygiene and disinfection, no stress.
Erysipelas: not a common disease, but found more in free range birds than in intensive units. The bird tends to be listless, and have swollen head and neck and swollen joints. Treat with penicillin. The infection is common to pigs and sheep

and is *dangerous* in that it is zoonotic i.e. transmissible to humans, so handle any sudden deaths with care.

Respiratory diseases

Due to the construction of a bird with many air spaces in the bird for lightness, any respiratory disease is magnified as it can be present throughout and not just in the lungs.

Sinusitis or Mycoplasma gallisepticum: **cause:** bacteria, spread via the egg or direct from bird to bird.

Symptoms: mucus in the corner of the eye, discharge from the nostrils, sneezing, rattling breathing, swollen sinuses - one or both. Mucky feathers where the bird has wiped its eyes. (Used to be known as roup).

Treatment: suppression of the symptoms achieved by use of Tylan either as an injection in the breast muscle and/or in the sinus, or added to the water. Birds remain carriers. Hard sinuses can be lanced and the cheesy material removed but this must be done by a vet.

Prevention: sufficient ventilation. Eradication of disease. Immunity is aquired.

Mycoplasma synoviae: **cause:** similar to ***gallisepticum***

Symptoms: similar to sinusitis but with lameness and swelling of joints, breast blisters, loss of weight and colour.

Treatment and Prevention: as ***gallisepticum.*** Affected birds are uneconomic.

Rhinotracheitis: symptoms are similar to mycoplasma but this kills. Mainly found in intensive systems, check with a specialist vet if you suspect this disease.

Aspergillosis: **cause:** fungus present in mouldy straw or mouldy feed.

Symptoms: respiratory distress and gasping.

Treatment: none. Removal of source of mould will help.

Prevention: Beware of mould. Use woodshavings for litter and keep it dry.

Worms: **cause:** 6 different types inhabiting different parts of the gut. Not so much a problem in fattening systems but affects free range birds and can stunt their growth.

Symptoms: lack of appetite, slow loss of weight, greenish droppings.

Treatment: Mebenvet, in the food. The only preparation which deals with all 6 types, unlike preparations which go in the water and do just gapeworm and roundworm.

Prevention: there is no such thing as clean ground as wild birds contaminate everything. Fresh ground helps. Immunity is aquired, although stress may cause an outbreak.

External parasites

Lice: Can be encountered in fattening birds. More a problem with breeding stock as a heavy infestation can result in infertility in the stags.

Symptoms: unthriftiness and mopeyness.

Treatment: individual birds have to be caught (see handling, pages 7, 39) and the vent area checked. You will see the yellow louse and in bad cases the white clusters of eggs (nits) on the base of the feathers, and often a flaking of the skin. Pull off the nits gently and dispose of them elsewhere (otherwise they will hatch out and start the whole cycle again). Sprinkle louse powder under the tail, under the wings, between the legs and on the back and rub in.

Prevention: stags should be checked or de-loused once a month, louse powder can be added to the nestboxes for the hens.

Red Mite: cause: can be picked up from wild birds.
Symptoms: unthriftiness and anaemia. White specks can be seen in the perch sockets and around the crevices. Any red specks with them are those mites full of blood. They suck the blood of the birds at night and spend the day hiding.
Treatment: spray the infected area with a fly spray and repeat a week later to catch any hatched in the meantime.
Prevention: spray ends of perches monthly.

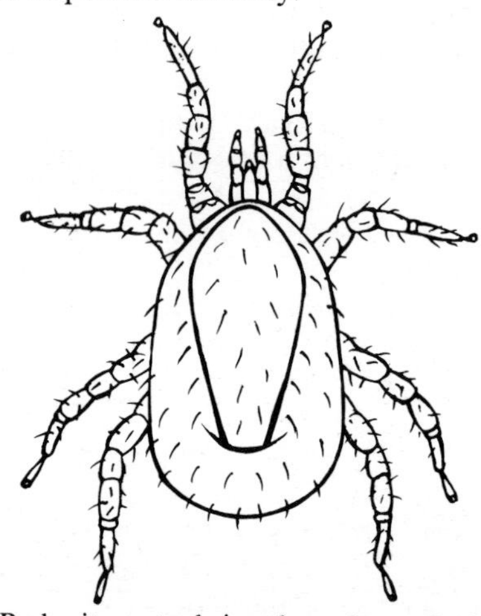

Dermanyssus gallinae Red mite, actual size about 1mm. Sucks blood at night, lives in cracks in the woodwork during the day - a whitish powder betrays its presence. Worst in warm weather. Makes the birds anaemic.

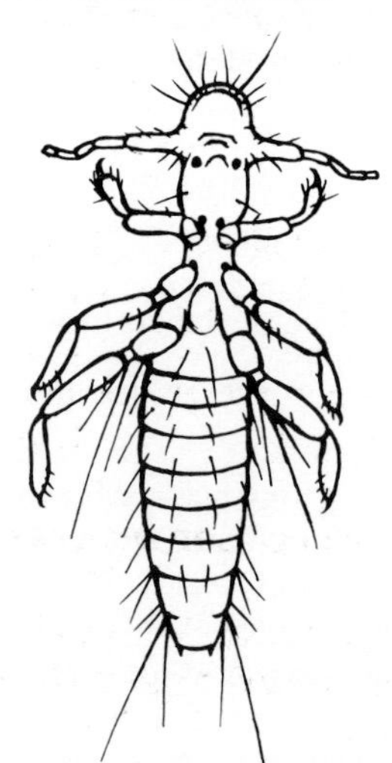

Menopon gallinae common fowl louse, lives on skin debris and feathers. Irritant. About 2mm long, yellow. Eggs (nits) are laid on feathers.

Injuries:
Breakages can occur occasionally if the birds have been panicked. If a leg is broken it can be set by using the plastic tube from a disposable syringe as a splint, cut down one side to get it on, packed with cotton wool and taped over the straightened break. Check particularly that it is not too tight or hot and remove after a month. A break on a joint usually means culling the bird. If a wing is broken, either cull the bird or if it is a valuable breeding bird, tape the wing to the body in the natural position until it is healed.

Young bronze turkey hen showing her leg set with a "syringe" splint. She had caught her leg in a fence, and subsequently went on to become a good breeding bird

Wounds:
Two main causes of wounds are feather-pecking and stags claws. Remove the wounded bird as soon as possible as the others will go for the blood, and spray the wound with a gentian violet antibiotic spray. Keep the bird separate until the wound has completely healed. On bad tears from stags claws the vet may be needed to stitch it up. Use saddles in future.

Poisoning:
Be aware that certain plants can poison such as foxglove, laurel, yew and laburnum.

NOTE: Britain has been free of NEWCASTLE DISEASE since 1986. This highly contagious respiratory disease is NOTIFIABLE. Inform your vet immediately or the Police.

Vaccines:
in use on commercial units against Erysipelas and Fowl Pox.

VERMIN

It is very important in planning and installing housing for rearing and breeding turkeys that you think about avoiding the problem of vermin. Care should be taken over the storage of feedstuffs and during the time of killing and processing the birds. Vermin can take the form of foxes, rats, wild birds, flies, mink, lice etc. We have written ***Modern Vermin Control*** (£3.50 inc. postage and packing from the Domestic Fowl Trust) which covers this subject in depth.

Bronze stag (DFT)

It has been the intention of this book not only to inspire you to keep turkeys but also to realise that their welfare is entirely under your control and your good stockmanship is the key to their welfare. A Welfare Code has been produced by involved organisations, obtainable from MAFF, and is essential reading for anyone wanting to keep turkeys.

USEFUL ADDRESSES AND SUPPLIERS

Agricultural Training Board, National Poultry Training Adviser, George Hall, York House, Clarendon Avenue, Leamington Spa CV32 5PP (0926) 421105

Antec International Ltd., Windham Road, Chilton Industrial Estate, Sudbury, Suffolk CO10 6XD. (0787) 77305. *Antec 250S and Virkon S.*

George H. Elt Ltd., Eltex Works, Bromyard Road, Worcester WR2 5DN. (0905) 422377. *Eltex Equipment.*

Gloucester Laboratories (Veterinary) Ltd., St. Oswalds Road, Cattle Market, Gloucester. GL1 2SJ. (0452) 24961. *Post mortem service.*

Danro Ltd., Unit 5, Oaks Industrial Estate, Station Road, Earl Shilton, Leicester LE9 7GA. (0455) 47061. *Package labelling.*

Bramley & Wellesley Ltd., Unit C, Chancel Close Trading Estate, Eastern Avenue, Gloucester. GL4 7SN. (0452) 300450. *Flexinet.*

National Farmer's Union, Agriculture House, Knightsbridge, London SW1X 7NJ.

MAFF (Publications), Lion House, Willowburn Estate, Alnwick, Northumberland NE66 2PF. *leaflets on all aspects of agriculture (also ADAS publications)*

Traditional Farm Fresh Turkey Association, Brecon, Chyngton Road, Seaford, Sussex BN25 4HH. (0323) 899802.

British Turkey Federation Ltd., High Holborn House, 52-54 High Holborn, London WC1V 6SX. 01 242 4683

Poultry World, Carew House, Wallington, Surrey SM6 0DX. 01 661 3500. *Monthly publication, subscription only. Has turkey suppliers.*

Domestic Fowl Trust, Honeybourne, Nr. Evesham, Worcestershire WR11 5QJ. (0386) 833083. *Housing, candler, pure turkey breeds, humane despatcher, Mebenvet.*

If you have any difficulty obtaining any of the products mentioned in this book please contact the Domestic Fowl Trust.

Relevant publications from MAFF

Welfare Code for Turkeys	Leaflet 704
Feeding turkeys	Leaflet 427
Diseases of turkeys	Leaflet 523
Blackhead	Leaflet 20
Rearing turkeys for meat production (ADAS)	P397
Poultry Nutrition	RB174
Turkey production: Breeding and husbandry	RB242
Turkey production: Health	RB243

Code of Practice for on farm slaughter and marketing of poultry (NFU)

INDEX